# Ancient History:

# THE

# TWENTIETH

# CENTURY

by

Avraham C. Ben-Yosef

# Ancient History:
# THE
# TWENTIETH
# CENTURY

by

## Avraham C. Ben-Yosef

Extending Horizons Books
Porter Sargent Publisher
11 Beacon St., Boston, Mass. 02108

Library of Congress Catalog Card Number 69-15529

One kind word can warm three winter months.

*—Japanese Proverb*

"To the memory of my father, Joseph Welsman, London, England, 1893-1929."

# Contents

# Preface: The Twentieth Century

The Age of Faith was followed by the Age of Reason. These were followed by the age of neither. They were replaced by a kind of purposeless, nihilist existentialism. Facts counted for little in the popular or political mind, being replaced by prejudices induced by commercial and social brainwashing (advertising and propaganda). Two trends arose, in separate blocs of countries. One trend may be identified as the Age of Commerce, of go-getting in the direction of money and status without the slightest idealist aim giving the frenzied activity any satisfying justification. In the opposing bloc, the trend can be termed the Age of Anti-commerce, an imposed centralized collectivism with little basis other than a materialistic pettiness parallel to its opposition. (This in spite of the originally worthy idealistic goals which inspired so-called communism.)

Nature abhorring a vacuum, the mental gap and lack of ideals was filled by a return to primitive passions, among which a tribalist, racial nationalism predominated. A Burmese Secretary-General of the rather ironically titled United Nations (an organization of ostensible mutual cooperation) said he heard that the consequent racial conflict must exceed in horrors the worst excesses of previous religious wars. He was right.

Such a negatively-based world civilization, split within itself, was doomed before it could begin to develop. Without an independently diversified but peacefully coordinated creative philosophy, human progress was blocked by senseless, vain, and suicidal conflict. Comparatively few ever dedicated their lives to true and permanent rebellion. But these few were laying the foundations of the finer future yet to dawn for troubled humanity.

vii

# Introduction

This is not a textbook for educatees of the first age-group (2-18), nor of the second (38-45), nor even for those on special courses at other ages. It is purely for the general reader, and is designed, above all, to give him, as far as possible, an impression of what it would feel like to live in the twentieth century.

As all writers of history know, it is extremely difficult to convey this "feel" of a period – all the more so if it is ancient or very ancient (the oldtime division between "B.C." and "A.D." makes a convenient division also between these two categories). In fact, the historian usually does not even attempt such a difficult task; he merely records facts, according to his own interpretation, and leaves the rest to his readers' imagination.

In the present instance, however, something different is being attempted. As far as may be, it is hoped to transport the reader back in time a millenium, so that in however slight and artificial a manner, he can, to some extent, grasp something of the atmosphere of the life and thought of the people of that time itself. Naturally, only a very small measure of success is conceivable, but this is understood from the outset.

While the basis of the book is inevitably direct interpretation of the results of historical research, for what it is worth, the method chosen for portrayal of the period under review is largely one of quotation from the relevant ancient literature. Only in the case of a few short extracts are these quotations attributable to named writers. For the most part, at any rate, the longer extracts are from sources where no author's name has come down to us, they being generally known only to a handful of scholars, since in virtually every case they have not survived complete. It is hoped that the presentation of this rare but significant material to the general public will prove of wide-spread interest and value.

To those readers who query why the twentieth, and not some other century, has been chosen for survey in this case, there is, of course, the obvious answer that this does not pretend to be other than one of the spate of books which are appearing these days now that we are entering upon the thirtieth century, the twentieth being the inevitable subject. It may be merely childish fantasy to be still attracted by mere round numbers, like a thousand, but even in these comparatively enlightened days, human sentiment still remains in plenty, and there seems no appreciable desire to abolish it, although with the latest techniques we possibly could if we tried.

But there is another reason. And this too is obvious enough. The twentieth century still holds, and will always hold, a special place in human history. It was the century of the two great world wars. And it was the century of the discovery of atomic energy, which on the one hand put an end to the disastrous period of world wars and which, on the other, solved the age-old power problem — or rather the problem of lack of power — which thereupon enabled modern civilization to arise. Previously, it must be remembered, power was obtained from quaint, primitive natural sources like coal and oil and so on, even if some was hydroelectric. Worse, quite an amount, laughable as it seems to us today, was obtained from the muscles of men and animals themselves. We must not forget, too, that they used to grow animals still in those days actually for human food, along with plants, as well as for power-supply, for synthetic foods had scarcely been invented. Indeed it all seems very strange to us today.

However, in spite of their overriding importance, we shall not be concerned primarily with the frightful wars and the early usage (and terrible misusage) of atomic energy which most characterized the twentieth century. We shall be much more concerned in this book with the extraordinary social atmosphere and outlook then prevailing. It was the period of nationalism *in excelsis* — of this mental disease's last and greatest epidemic spread, when our little home-planet was cut up into between a hundred and two hundred separate "countries" or "nations" as they were then called, each not only with its own governmental organization but with its own highly dangerous collection of arma-ments. Obviously, in such ludicrous circumstances, wars of all sorts could hardly be avoided. But what we want to convey to the reader above all is the peculiar mental attitude of that time (and, admittedly, of previous ones from earliest days, if not always so strongly expressed) which is summed up in the ancient term, "patriotism." This is a complex phenomenon, which actually includes some worthy motives, such as loyalty to fine causes. But it was so mixed up with primitive differentiation-aggression that it became the curse of the age. Little real human progress could be made until the break-through at the end of the century under review, which, of course, marks the beginning of the modern period of civilization under rational world government.

We know now that the irrationality of the ancient regime was basically due to the formidable excess voltages of the D-waves in the brain, as found nowadays in the more ferocious wild animals brought in for test. These naturally gave rise to fearful aggression-phenomena, which in modern times we permanently neutralize within a few days after birth by suitable electrical injection to the infant brain. But since nothing of these matters had been discovered in ancient times, most peculiar social phenomena ensued, and it is these which will comprise our main focus of interest. There was the virtually incredible East-West clash, or Capitalist-Communist conflict, as it was variously called. (There were, in fact, all kinds of other strange titles for this most remarkable huge-scale human misunderstanding.) This must not be confused with the important differences between the so-called Eastern and Western civilizations of that period. Communism (which in any case it was not) was purely a part of the Western civilization, although sometimes tacked on to the Eastern one! And all this was merely the beginning of the twentieth-century wonderland.

In the West, for instance, there was the astounding craze for private cars, of extremely limited practical utility, owing to overcrowding on the roads, but of immense social status significance, and obviously a superb outlet for the aggression-energy of the deadly D-waves. (These cars were lethal instruments, producing an incessant and tremendous death toll, plus millions of wounded.) There was the peculiar and almost universal drug-addiction to tobacco, which was smoked in the mouth with the aid of contrivances to hold it. Even today, we do not altogether know the cause, in terms of nerve-voltages, for this strange addiction, which persisted for centuries before finally dying out, it having come down from very primitive times indeed.

What is most important from our point of view is that these two intensely damaging habits alone gave rise to some of the mightiest industries known, even on modern scales. These were supported by a colossal barrage of brain-washing called advertising which involved and

distorted the mental power of entire continental populations. To the
mentally healthy people of today, no one individual from among whom
would ever dream of copying another just for the sake of "being in the
swim," such phenomena seem nightmarish.

# 1 The Social Position

The difficulty of transporting oneself back in imagination a thousand years to the twentieth century is even greater than in the case of most other centuries. For human civilization then was in a peculiar state of development (largely backwards), which has not quite been paralleled before or since.

Ostensibly, there were two civilizations prevailing at the time, Western and Eastern. The former comprised the cultural heritage and way of life of the comparatively developed regions, mostly in the Northern Hemisphere, but partially excluding East Asia, while the term "Eastern" was often understood in a somewhat geographical sense and implied most of the rest of the world's peoples. These latter were the great majority, and lived with much less science than even the so-called West.

While there were very important philosophical elements in the Eastern civilization, the fact is that they were not incorporated in a materially efficient style of life, even by the standards of those days. Consequently, the whole of this civilization, in spite of the wealth of its valuably intuitive tradition, was nearly always regarded as backward by the Westerners. In a purely practical sense, they were right. The West had little alternative but to spread their more modern techniques all around the planet; in so doing they very nearly swamped the Eastern civilization altogether. Not quite, though, for the latter was essentially a mental phenomenon. Western civilization, if one wants to be cynical about it, could not altogether unfairly be regarded as anti-mental. (However, the term must not be taken literally; its implications will be manifested later.) The Western veneer soon became much more than a mere veneer. It infiltrated internally and deeply, and in the end only a limited amount was left of the Eastern mental outlook. This finally reacted back on the West, until the modern world synthesis was achieved. But in order to simplify matters as far as possible, it will be sufficient for us in this survey of the twentieth century to concentrate our attention on its Western civilization for the most part; occasional references to the Eastern outlook will have to serve. It is not contended that this amounts to a balanced treatment, but it is the only way to avoid becoming hopelessly unwieldy. The Western civilization was, after all, very definitely predominant in that twentieth century.

But it was declining. As in the case of other civilizations, it is impossible to pinpoint its peak and date the decline precisely. The peak was presumably around the very beginning of the century, but there was development after that as well. Naturally, it all depends on which basis one chooses as standards of judgment — morality, art, or what you will. Twentieth century science went on to very late development indeed, compared with more humanistic aspects; but no one today would judge a civilization on its science.

Our difficulties are therefore especially great. This was indeed a transition century, more so than the preceding one. The two of them together, at any rate, constitute the change-over period from almost pre-scientific times to the modern age (in its elementary beginnings). For the reader of a thousand years afterwards, therefore, it is no easy matter to know where to draw the line between ancient and modern: the line itself is blurred. Moreover there are the previous lines of division we sketched: the line between Western and Eastern civilization and that between rise and fall. These, too, are at least as blurred.

The mixture of facts, events and outlooks in the period chosen for study is indeed bewildering. It is extremely difficult even to attempt to categorize matters. Sometimes one can read a contemporary work of that time and feel relatively at home with it. But one can pick up another book or journal dating back to the twentieth century and feel one is in a dream world of virtual madness.

The latter impression was not, in fact, unknown even to those alive then. So it will be well for us to resolve our difficulties as far as we may by going straight back to contemporary accounts and gaining, in some slight measure, the feel of things as they appeared to particularly advanced minds of that age. The first extract is from a book by an outstanding psychologist-sociologist of the mid-twentieth century, Erich Fromm. He very meaningfully called his book *The Sane Society*, and, after referring to the terrible warlikeness of men at that time, he wrote:

In these outbursts of destructiveness and paranoid suspicion, however, we are not behaving differently from what the civilized part of mankind has done in the last three thousand years of history. According to Victor Cherbulliez, from 1500 B.C. to 1860 A.D. no less than about eight thousand peace treaties were signed, each one supposed to secure permanent peace, and each one lasting on an average two years!

Our direction of economic affairs is scarcely more encouraging. We live in an economic system in which a particularly good crop is often an economic disaster, and we restrict some of our agricultural productivity in order to 'stabilise the market,' although there are millions of people who do not have the very things we restrict, and who need them badly. Right now our economic system is functioning very well, because, among other reasons, we spend billions of dollars per year to produce armaments. Economists look with some apprehension to the time when we stop producing armaments, and the idea that the state should produce houses and other useful and needed things instead of weapons easily provokes accusations of endangering freedom and individual initiative.

We have a literacy above 90 percent of the population. We have radio, television, movies, a newspaper a day for everybody. But instead of giving us the best of past and present literature and music, these media of communication, supplemented by advertising, fill the minds of men with the cheapest trash, lacking in any sense of reality, with sadistic phantasies which a half-way cultured person would be embarassed to entertain even once in a while. But while the mind of everybody, young and old, is thus poisoned, we go on blissfully to see to it that no "immorality" occurs on the screen. Any suggestion that the government should finance the production of movies and radio programs which would enlighten and improve the minds of our people would be met again with indignation and accusations in the name of freedom and idealism.

We have reduced the average working hours to about half what they were one hundred years ago. We today have more free time available than our forefathers dared to dream of. But what has happened? We do not know how to use the newly gained free time; we try to kill the time we have saved, and are glad when another day is over.

Why should I continue with a picture which is known to everybody? Certainly, if an individual acted in this fashion, serious doubts would be raised as to his sanity; should he, however, claim that there is nothing wrong, and that he is acting perfectly reasonably, then the diagnosis would not even be doubtful any more.

It should be explained at this point that our author was specifically describing the position in his own country, the United States of America, or the southern half (for the most part) of the North American continent. But the fact that Erich Fromm based his remarks locally is immaterial in this context. They applied equally well to twentieth century Western civilization as a whole, except that section then variously known as Socialist or Communist, where the situation was somewhat different. Reference to this state of affairs will be made later.

Before taking temporary leave of this author, of special significance to every student of the twentieth century, it is appropriate to make one more quotation from the book mentioned, by way of a first-class example of an ancient statement with which we can feel perfectly at home even today:

> ... What would be the structure of a sane society? First of all, a society in which no man is a means toward another's ends, but always and without exception an end in himself; hence, where nobody is used, nor uses himself for purposes which are not those of the unfolding of his own human powers; where man is the center, and where all economic and political activities are subordinated to the aim of his growth. A sane society is one in which qualities like greed, exploitativeness, possessiveness, narcissism, have no chance to be used for greater material gain or for the enhancement of one's personal prestige. Where acting according to one's conscience is looked upon as a fundamental and necessary quality and where opportunism and lack of principles is deemed to be asocial; where the individual is concerned with social matters so that they become personal matters, where his relation to his fellow man is not separated from his relationship in the private sphere. A sane society, furthermore, is one which permits man to operate within manageable and observable dimensions, and to be an active and

responsible participant in the life of society, as well as the master
of his own life. It is one which furthers human solidarity and not
only permits but stimulates its members to relate themselves to
each other lovingly; a sane society furthers the productive activity
of everybody in his work, stimulates the unfolding of reason and
enables man to give expression to his inner needs in collective art
and rituals.

A thousand years later, the only possible comment is that we can
hardly better such a statement, even in our own quite well-ordered
times.

Before we enter upon a slight discussion of what was fairly
commonly admitted even then as a moral breakdown of society in a
period of great scientific progress – the essence of the decline of that
Western civilization – it would be desirable to deepen to a considerable
extent our concept of the social atmosphere of the twentieth century
by quoting from another, very much less prominent, contemporary
social critic. This excerpt is taken from a rare, small-scale, privately-
produced magazine of the mid-century called *Ahimsa Progress,* and was
written by its editor, Arthur J. Kelly. (The word "Ahimsa" comes from
the very ancient Sanskrit language, meaning "harmlessness," and at that
time denoted the central doctrine of a small group of people, essentially
from among the Anglo-Saxons, who, horrified at the characteristic
callousness and cruelty of their civilization, formed a strictly vegetarian
society, refusing to harm animals or other people.)

What of the masses who provide the labour and the mental
stress around which this monolith we still call civilisation winds
its stifling shackles? What say have they in the progress of the
community or indeed in the organisation of their own lives? Who
among herded humanity is fortunate enough to see inspiration
amongst the morass of mediocrity and subjugation of individuality?

We have, sadly, reached that stage of evolution where few
individuals are valued in themselves in such a way that they
cannot be readily replaced. It is too expensive to be unique. In
the time it taks a craftsman to create an object which is a thing of
beauty as well as utility, a machine will produce a thousand,
stamped out with unerring precision and monotony, and fed on
the vast conveyor belts which are the life blood of this top-heavy

society to the stereotyped minds that lie like doomed prisoners in the gloomy shades of bodies tied to an endless round of work, sleep and play. The natural environment has been destroyed, and in its place we have a panorama of brick and tarmac interspersed with dreary parks and gardens that look more and more like plastic as grass gives way to lawn and our majestic trees give way to flowering inverted umbrellas.

Far from the places where nature is still permitted to weave her sacred spell of verdant pasture, gold, white and green again with reassuring timelessness, man collects her gems, distorts them until they become garish baubles and displays them in a hideous blaze of discordance in the tiny plot of ground he owns by courtesy of Messrs. Building Profits, Limited. These are the lucky ones, house-owning, or at least within some twenty years of being in that fabulous position. Others must accept the temporary loan of a council house because they are underpaid, while others still can hope for nothing better than a dingy room or part of a room and an irate landlady.

What has life to offer for those millions of beings who provide the main part of the productive labour upon which the monolith rests? The average man with only average intelligence and average parents gets little encouragement or incentive to strive for higher things. He enters school in a soulless industrial town and consciously or otherwise, competes fiercely for what education is available, only to discover that his average abilities afford him only average opportunities and therefore approximately half of average pay. He is doomed to a life of poverty or endless overtime or both, sapping his energies both physically and culturally.

He has a wife and usually two children to support, and can offer them nothing better than to keep their heads above water in the same endless rut; he can offer them no capital sum, he will not win the football pools and he could offer them nothing in any way spectacular in their genetic makeup. He can only admit to his children that in the mad rat race they have been born to be losers. His relaxation is conditioned by his lack of time, lack of drive and lack of education. He turns to drink, mainly for company and escape, whereupon society shows its disapproval by heavy taxation; he smokes, again incurring the wrath of the Treasury and a bonus in the way of cancer of the lungs and other diseases. He sacrifices what remains of his life in mute supplication to the idiot's lantern until his thoughts are those of the tinsel God and his millions of degenerate addicts, and lastly, in his mad frenzy, he drives his hire-purchase car in insatiable fury to the horizon — any horizon — to escape the drab monotony that was his death sentence at the moment of his birth. And as his mind is thwarted and distorted by mechanisation of all that was once enjoyably primitive, he resigns himself to accept a mounting cloud of oblivion and hours in a doctor's waiting room in exchange for a bewildering range of tranquilizers and a faint hint of pseudosanity.

Hard, embittered words indeed, and we should hope that they were exaggerated. Perhaps, as regards part of the middle classes of those days in industrial society, they were. But in regard to the extremely extensive lower sections of those classes, let alone all those in near-poverty and actual poverty, they must have been only too true; even understated. There are some interesting differences between this excerpt and the first we quoted from Erich Fromm. On this occasion lack of time, and not its excess, is referred to, and there is a special bias towards wild nature — certainly healthy enough on that industrial background. But we must leave the smaller points to our readers to ponder, and turn to the broader considerations involved.

The best way we can do this is to provide another quotation from a named source. In this case, we turn back to the North American region. The previous quotation, incidentally, was taken from the British section of the European region, and this fact alone can account for a good deal of the difference in style and content which we noted above. For back in the twentieth century, the British islands, with their remarkable history having produced a very special and isolated variant of European civilization, had not been rejoined to the European continent by the appropriate atomic operation which added the Dogger area to that continent. So the special British approach to matters, a unique mental attitude based on the peculiar social outlook there prevailing, was still in full force and influenced all the local writing quite considerably. We shall have occasion to make special reference to the remarkable British social phenomenon at a later stage.

The quotation we present now is relatively well known to students, for it was a most exceptional confession to be made in its time and place. The author was the famous professor of economics at the University of Chicago, Frank Hyneman Knight. He wrote a book of

essays which was called *The Ethics of Competition and Other Essays,*
but which in fact comprised mainly complex technical writing on
economic subjects. The title essay was not in the least characteristic,
but it was amazingly frank, and almost more amazingly, was frankly
placed in the most prominent position.

Before reproducing it, it is worth commenting that in the most
stereotyped national society of all in the Western civilization of that
period, the North American one, the most extraordinary freedom of
expression, although not complete, did prevail. What is much more
important, though, is that this did not make the slightest difference to
anything. The established order went on, scarcely anyone paying the
slightest attention to the intensive criticism sometimes publicly brought
against it. Social inertia was not the full explanation. The public had
long been trained, both in the schools when young and afterwards
continuously by the mass media of communication, (itself to an
overwhelming extent in "safe" hands) not to take seriously or even read
or listen to at all, social criticism of a pointed nature. The latter was
generally regarded as foolish, unbased, inaccurate, cranky, potentially
damaging to the stability of society, irrelevant, and so on, and was very
easily dismissed by those in controlling positions. The political myth
that all was for the best in the best of all possible worlds, apart,
perhaps, from a few slight irregularities needing attention in the near
future (easily promised, if requisite, and as quickly forgotten), was in
full sway. There was no difficulty at all in the case of a population
which, by our standards, was barely educated. Besides, between half
and three-quarters of that population was definitely well off in material
terms, even by modern standards, and certainly in the conditions of
those times; they were not inclined to interfere with prosperity, such as
it was. The unfortunate minority, far less favored, had neither the
cultural understanding nor the political power to change anything
anyway.

And here is the quotation itself:

> . . . there is truth in the allegation that unregulated competi-
> tion places a premium on deceit and corruption. In any case,
> where the family is the social unit, the inheritance of wealth,
> culture, educational advantages and economic opportunities tend
> toward the progressive increase of inequality, with bad results for
> personality at both ends of the scale. It is plainly contrary to fact
> to treat the individual as a datum, and it must be conceded that

the lines along which a competitive economic order tends to form character are often far from being ethically ideal. . . The ownership of personal or material productive capacity is based upon a complex mixture of inheritance, luck and effort, probably in that order of relative importance. What is the ideal distribution from the standpoint of absolute ethics may be disputed, but of the three considerations named certainly none but the effort can have ethical validity. . . (The) outcome (of business as a competitive game) is a very inaccurate test of real ability, for the terms on which different individuals enter the contest are too unequal. The luck element moreover is so large – far larger than fairly successful participants in the game will ever admit – that capacity and effort may count for nothing. And this luck element works cumulatively, as in gambling games generally. . . Admitting that business success tends in the large to go with business ability, we must face the question of the abstract merit of such capacity as a human trait, and hence of business as a game. It can hardly be denied that there is a preponderance of cultivated opinion against it. Successful businessmen have not become proverbial for the qualities that the best minds and most sensitive spirits of the race agree in calling noble. Business as it is and has been does not commonly display a very high order of sportsmanship. . .

We shall dismiss the subject by quoting a statement by Ruskin, which can hardly be waived aside as valueless or unrepresentative. 'In a community regulated by laws of demand and supply, but protected from open violence,' he says, 'the persons who become rich are, generally speaking, industrious, resolute, proud, covetous, prompt, methodical, sensible, unimaginative, insensitive and ignorant. The persons who remain poor are the entirely foolish, the entirely wise, the idle, the reckless, the humble, the thoughtful, the dull, the imaginative, the sensitive, the well-informed, the improvident, the irregularly and impulsively wicked, the clumsy knave, the open thief, the entirely merciful, just and godly person.'

However favourable an opinion one may hold of the business game, he must be very illiberal not to concede that others have a right to a different view and that large numbers of admirable people do not like the game at all. It is then justifiable at least to regard as unfortunate the dominance of the business game over life, the virtual identification of social living with it, to the extent that has come to pass in the modern world. In a social order where all values are reduced to the money measure in the degree that this is true of modern industrial nations, a considerable fraction of the most noble and sensitive characters will lead unhappy and even futile lives. Everyone is compelled to play the economic game and be judged by his success in playing it, whatever his field of activity or type of interest, and has to squeeze in as a side line any other competition, or non-competitive activity, which may have for him a greater intrinsic appeal... In America, particularly, where competitive business, and its concomitant, the sporting view of life, have reached their fullest development, there have come to be two sorts of virtue. The greatest virtue is to win; and meticulous questions about the methods are not in the best form, provided the methods bring victory. The lesser virtue is to go out and die gracefully after having lost...

A strong argument for cooperation, if it would work, would be its tendency to teach people to like each other in a more positive sense than can ever be bred by participation in a contest — certainly in a contest in which the means of life, or of a decent life, are felt to be at stake.

These were fine words indeed, and it is not surprising that they have gone ringing down the centuries among students of social history. They certainly open up our subject to its full essential expanse, and we cannot but honor the deep humanity of the learned professor who was clearly moved to reveal what the vast majority of his colleagues and contemporaries either deliberately kept quiet or never managed to realize. Before taking leave of this fine figure in his age, we shall permit ourselves one further quotation from his same essay, for it adds further basic considerations:

... Critical attention has been focussed, not merely on the glaring discrepancy between the actual principles of social action and the ethical-religious pretensions of Western civilisation, but also on the practical consequences which follow from the Machiavellian-Mandevillian standards which make intelligent selfishness equivalent to virtue, and power and cunning the main components of our human ideal... There is more willingness to envisage a world presenting less "progress" towards goals which

seem dubious, and a lower rate of consumption of "goods and services" whose connection with goodness and serviceability is not always clear. . .
'There is much to be said on both sides.'

This last remark may seem to us today rather generous. Yet there was something in it then – something serious. The men of those times were in a great quandary, which it took further centuries to solve entirely, although workable half-and-half solutions were in operation over wide areas before the twentieth century came to an end. Their great difficulty lay in their being almost entirely incapable of conceiving a non-dictatorial society without an economic system which included private enterprise and a competitive market in almost everything (including works of art!) on a general monetary basis. This was, of course, the essence of the famous East-West clash of the time, which we shall treat in more detail when we come to consider the political situation in the twentieth century world. All we need emphasize here is that both sides achieved remarkable failures. We must realize, however, that until modern science made adequate plenty freely available for all, thus making money obsolete, the difficulty was, up to a point, genuine. Goods being relatively scarce, they either had to be competed for or distributed from above. The first or Western way produced perhaps the most peculiar caricature of human society ever known. It brought about a predominantly widespread, although fortunately not complete, replacement of human values by money values, with very nearly fatal consequences. The second or Eastern way produced inadequately-based and inefficiently executed plans of distribution of equally unsatisfactorily designed production for several decades. Fundamentally the Eastern scheme was more logically humanistic, but owing to sheer lack of social technique (due to a misunderstanding, or no understanding at all, of human psychology) it was carried out with varying degrees of dictatorship which not infrequently reached such levels of brutality that the results were, in some cases, far worse even than in the West itself.

The consequent comi-tragedy, certainly exceedingly painful to those who suffered under it, drove very many people on both sides to mentally fling up their hands in despair, and take no further interest in the proceedings. In other words, they resigned from human life. They commonly retreated into their immediate families, and completely shed any (usually very slight) degree of social interest they may have had before. They felt themselves to be too small to have any influence on the course of affairs. This was when the Western political democracy lost virtually all real content and became a mere empty framework which the mass of the people had no serious interest in filling with content and operating. Naturally they fell easy prey to the machinations of the mass-advertising private enterprisers, themselves largely organized in dictatorial monopolies, or partial ones; and, being, for the most part, although by no means entirely, fed on adequate supplies of even cake, let alone bread, in the favoured, developed areas, as well as being plied with a surfeit of circuses, of the most vulgar quality imaginable, their degeneration was inevitable. The decline of their civilization does, in fact, demand further explanation, for we have not yet touched the central problem of why often very well educated people, let alone the others, accepted all this so supinely. But we shall reach this point a little later. For the moment, we need merely add that social endeavor differed over long periods from sector to sector, and, after the first revolutionary fervor wore off, it was generally little better in the Eastern Bloc. This seems surprising in view of the more logical structure of these deliberately designed societies and their directly high humanistic ideals, as originally expressed. It is clear that there was a failure to rise to the occasion — one of the greatest pities in human history. As far as we can judge at this distance of time, it seems that the goals set were too high for men to achieve in that comparatively early period of social evolution. They had not the moral strength or the powers of self-abnegation to harness themselves to great purposes. Moreover, as we mentioned before, the social designing was often frankly bad and, in fact, made impossible demands.

We know from subsequent history that a way out was eventually found: that the Western and Eastern Blocs of the Western civilization gradually progressed to a world merger in which the old, static Eastern civilization finally disappeared. The result was a new civilization altogether — the beginning of our own effective global one. The non-exploitation of man by man, the idea nominally enshrined in the ideals of the Eastern bloc, became a reality by the gradual abolition of all private employment and of all public employment not effectively run by self-governing groups. Today we cannot conceive how it could ever have been considered acceptable for one man to employ another, or many others, in exchange for a monetary wage. To us, this is only a different form of slavery. The paid employee had to obey his employer, and obedience to the will of another is in any case slavery in the humanist-moral sense. Slavery, as we know, had been the bane of civilization from its inception; more, it had constituted the very root of it, and still did in the twentieth century. Private employment in the Western Bloc was offset by public employment in the Eastern; both were continuations of previous slavery and subsequent serfdom in very ancient and ancient civilizations. Neither afforded generally significant individual freedom, although both sides hotly contended that they did. However, the Western Bloc did allow wider ranges of choice than the more strictly controlled and at first much less developed Eastern Bloc areas could. Although much, if not most, of the much-vaunted Western freedom was so pseudo- as to be imaginary, some did exist, and was quite important enough in its formulation (if not very often in its execution) to constitute an essential, basic element in the more elevated society-to-be.

Each side, therefore, made its contribution to the final solution, the thought of Western civilization having to split into the two blocs in order to tread the painful road to a satisfactory synthesis, reunited. By the time it got there, the old Eastern civilization had been eliminated entirely (and the whole world modernized, as we have stressed) but not without making its own vital contribution from its deeper intuitive level of philosophical thought — essential for arriving at a good minimum level of human values. It is curious to note that in spite of the admirable intentions of the Eastern Bloc leaders, it was in the Western Bloc that far and away the greatest strides in philosophical thought, incorporating the significant items from that of Eastern civilization, were made at first. Only later did the Eastern Bloc catch up in this regard and become fluid enough in its outlook to learn from the older East as well. It is because the Western Bloc was less directly doctrinaire, in spite of its professions typically being betrayed by its actions, that it scored a point over the Eastern Bloc for quite a time, and even received a flow of discouraged refugees from the latter. But its artificiality and insincerity made it impossible to hold firm indefinitely; the ultimate collapse of its basic system was unavoidable.

The Eastern Bloc was temporarily held back in its outlook by the burden of its totalitarian planning, actually quite beyond human capacity at that time. Not until it replaced centralization by decentralization, thus reaching effective democracy, could its people compete adequately in the mental field with their Western opposite numbers, who at least enjoyed a very considerably decentralized organization already, even if its democracy was largely sham. There was at any rate a certain feeling of freedom in the mentally alive circles of the Western Bloc, and there was much less official censorship than in the Eastern one, insecurely struggling to establish a new social order. Hence the temporary advantage of the Westerners was solid; but in the nature of the case, as the Easterners developed on all fronts, it could not endure.

As it was, life in general must have been very uncomfortable on both sides then, except, of course, for favored groups here and there. An ancient manuscript states that there was a joke current clandestinely in the Eastern Bloc to the effect that in the West there was exploitation of man by man — and in the East, the opposite! We can still smile at that in our happier age; but, in that it expressed the truth, we can only pity the unfortunates of a millenium ago, and yet admire them for their brave courage in having enough sense of humor to laugh at themselves.

We have gradually been leading up to the central point of this chapter, but in order to point it still more intensively, we propose to retrace our footsteps for a short time and approach our objective from a different angle. Let us therefore return to the last quotation we reproduced — from the work of Professor Knight — and examine it more closely.

When the professor refers to the glaring discrepancy between actual social-action principles and the then current ethical-religious pretensions, he reveals the fatal hypocrisy almost universally prevailing: the basic insincerity of twentieth century society. Both in West and East, its people lived a great lie. And this inner rottenness naturally guaranteed the downfall of that century's civilization; not by any means the first such instance, as is well known.

For the most part, our initial approach has been sociological, although not devoid of moral overtones and even direct mention of the moral issue on which we now focus specifically. (Professor Knight used the actual word "virtue.") It is in this field that we touch the essence of the matter as nearly as may be. The problem obviously is to explain why this moral collapse ensued. Certainly there was no single reason, but a whole complex of reasons. The decline in religious belief, in face of scientific advance, played a part, owing to the connection with ethics, but insofar as religion was typically kept in a separate compartment of the individual mind from that dealing with everyday life, its direct influence should not be exaggerated. Most puzzling is the decline in what must simply be called common decency. It is not that previous centuries reached any great moral heights in the public domain. Rather the contrary. Yet the records rarely show personal callousness, lack of social cohesion and responsibility — such an atomization of society — to anything like the extent we are bound to note in researching the century under review. Uncontrolled techno-logical progress along with great population increase and ludicrously inadequate education (barely including the subject of citizenship at all) were bound to bring about disorder. But even all these and still various other causes can hardly satisfy us as to the inner reasons for the rot.

We may feel we are putting our fingers more accurately on the source of the trouble if we refer in a word to "commercialization." It is here that Professor Knight's mention of " 'goods and services' whose connection with goodness and serviceability is not always clear" gives the clue. The mass-production of private-enterprise Capitalism was meant to bring the blessings of plenty to all men. But owing to the failure to distribute the products equitably, either regionally or globally, the blessing became a curse, and the spirit of man was cheapened together with the goods, which thus became "bads."

They used to have a saying then, which already dated some way back in the past and in fact tended to lose its force in the twentieth century itself: "Money is the root of all evil." The statement is very definitely an exaggeration, obviously; but unfortunately, money probably was the root of most of the evil of that time, and in this we arrive at the crux of the matter as far as it can probably ever be revealed to us now. We cannot conceive today how it was that money dominated almost every human life then, for we have saner social arrangements altogether. The Communist idea of free distribution according to need, even if limited to modest but fair shares at first, had indeed already been mooted; but in spite of governmental nomen-clature, it was never carried out in the twentieth century, except in certain intensely significant small groups to which we shall give extensive attention as we draw to our conclusion. The Socialist or Eastern Bloc did try to limit the influence of money by supplying many social services over and above wages. To a mostly much smaller extent, the Western Bloc, especially in its Welfare State development, did the same. But in the West, this was totally insufficient to detract attention from money-making; and in the East, although intentions and early practice were better, in the end Western influence was too strong and the Eastern Bloc peoples also succumbed to this same social disease. Commercialism, materialism in the sense of overriding ambition to attain more and more material goods and accompanying social status — it little matters which term is used. Money was the fetish,

Mammon the god; the consequent false values precipitated that moral collapse which is our central point here.

Certainly money has played a vital part in the development of civilization; even today we keep accounts for control purposes. But of course we have taken money out of private hands, where it is far too dangerous owing to its psychological effects and the power complexes it so easily produces, matters we are not yet able to deal with by electrical treatment of the brain. Even when we do arrive at such technique, however, we shall not return to the general use of money. In the eyes of modern men, it will always seem primitive now. In earlier centuries than the twentieth, it was undoubtedly a source of evil, but for the most part it was a good servant. By mid-twentieth century, it had clearly become master. And such a bad master was it that it succeeded in bringing an end to that century's civilization.

There was another professor of that age, Tawney, who suggested that the attraction of running a business lay probably more in power than in profits, which certainly bears out what we have just expressed. Here and there, there was indeed a consciousness of what was going on. And it is only because a few people did manage to see this that eventually the way was found, in future generations, for a happier social order. A very relevant contemporary extract is that which follows from a book called *The Morality of Punishment* by A. C. Ewing.

It is not good that material wealth and real worth should be correlated in people's minds; it greatly increases the desire for the former and consequently promotes the evils which moralists are so fond of describing as characteristic of 'this money-loving age.'

It is important to note that, in so far as the wealth acquired by a man in the ordinary processes of business is regarded as a reward, it tends to confuse real public service with the acquisition of money for oneself. From the mere fact that a man makes a profit of ten thousand pounds a year we cannot tell how much of that sum comes from really serving the public and how much from outdoing rivals in a way which does not serve the public at all. In so far as the profit is made by a supply of better goods, a public service is being rewarded, though probably to excess; in so far as it is made by a more ingenious use of advertisements than his rivals are capable of, something is being rewarded which is hardly public service at all; in so far as it is made by cornering a commodity, using sweated labour, or by tricking rivals and customers, a reward is being conferred for what is the reverse of a service. Yet others, having no chance of distinguishing how much of the profit is due to each of these factors, only know that the man has had the ability to make a profit of ten thousand pounds and will tend to estimate him in proportion to his wealth, not in proportion to his real public service, since they have no means of judging that except from his wealth.

Unless he passes beyond certain very wide limits in the means he uses, a man attains as much honour through making a fortune in ways that are of very little benefit (or none at all) to the public as he does through making it only by the supply of a real need at a fair price. This is no doubt one of the reasons for the strength of the tendency to treat money-making in business as the end, rather than public service. Money becomes the aim rather than service, partly because it is treated as the measure of service without really being so.

It is a more disputable question whether these or equally bad drawbacks depend on our particular economic system, or, human nature being what it is, are inevitable under any system. Any all-pervasive system of pecuniary rewards must tend in the direction of identifying the acquisition of money with the rendering of service in the public estimation, and by making the former an honour, increase man's natural love of material wealth. . .

If we turn back for a moment to the professors of that period, there was another one of them who rubbed things in rather forcibly, if also very artistically, if we may say so. This was Professor K. Smellie in his *Reason in Politics*:

. . . the elements of social decency were found to be beyond the power of the market to provide: pauperism, education and the essentials of public health became the responsibility of the State; then it was found that the continuous plebiscite of the consumer was counteracted by the continuous propaganda of the producer, and that the State must penetrate into every interstice of the economic web if fraud and even violence were not to be used more widely and unscrupulously by the princelets of property than they had ever been by principalities and powers.

As a matter of fact, a great man of a slightly earlier period had virtually prophesied all this beforehand. He was Abraham Lincoln, and we have on record this profound statement of his:

> I see in the near future a crisis approaching that unnerves me and causes me to tremble for the safety of my country. . . Corporations have been enthroned, an era of corruption in high places will follow, and the money power of the country will endeavor to prolong its reign by working upon the prejudices of the people until the wealth is aggregated in a few hands, and the republic is destroyed.

Why did well-educated, understanding people accept all this so supinely? It is evident that they felt themselves as helpless before mass forces as Abraham Lincoln himself apparently did. When attempts were, in fact, made to erect a finer social order, economic difficulties were in no small measure overcome by means of varying degrees of planning and control, but nowhere, it seems, could the socio-moral decline be checked substantially, if at all. Social structure did not permit it.

What was involved here? Not only the money system and the accompanying class phenomena, but the cultural set-up, or lack of it, including especially education, had a very great deal to do with it. In the West, the amount of advertising in the press, on radio and television, was so vast that we can have no conception of it today. Nor can we conceive the degree of its inanity, due to the absence of any serious education among the masses of most peoples. The whining voices (presumably meant to be wheedling ones) preserved for us on ancient recordings of the "light" radio programs and TV of those days (and only these indeed light programs were ever listened to by most of the populations of most regions, as far as we can estimate, since cultural standards were commonly too low for anything better) would have been impossible for cultivated people to tolerate, even then. The worst newspapers comprised almost entirely advertisements — and even in the best ones, the "news" consisted essentially of the decisions of a few politicians (not, of course, statesmen-philosophers) here and there in the world. Real news of research, development, public happenings and so on, appeared secondarily, if at all, in most papers, as far as we can judge from surviving copies, but in all those of mass-circulation, crime and scandal chased even politicians off the pages.

The Western educational picture of that period is scarcely less incredible. Its inadequacies became so apparent by the middle of the twentieth century that appreciable experimentation and actual improvement set in, apparently because the Eastern Bloc had already energetically achieved considerable progress, although we think there were internal drives as well, mostly based on developing technology. The whole subject is too vast for us to go into in detail, and we must refer readers to histories of education through the ages which pay particular attention to the peculiar state of affairs prevailing in the twentieth century, with its famous "Two Cultures" phenomenon and other gravely undesirable manifestations. From our point of view, education then would seem to have been deliberately designed to keep people ignorant, rather than the reverse. The middle-life period of education, universal with us, was unknown to the ancients. They based everything upon strange systems of examinations, which called for a mixture of strong nerves and mental agility as well as for some actual knowledge. There were no world tours for students, except for a handful with remarkably rich parents. One must remember that the round-the-world railway lines, did not even exist then. It is only in recent centuries, with the completion of the Behring Straits Tunnel and others, together with the construction of the new continents, that this vital educational facility became a reality. One could go on and on with this theme, but space does not permit. The cardinal point, in any case, is that education beyond the most elementary remained the preserve of very small percentages in most populations throughout the twentieth century, although improvement did set in towards the end.

But to sum up the educational position in most of the Western world at that time, one cannot do better than again quote from a contemporary critic. In this case it is Harold Laski, whose *Reflections on the Revolution of our Time* are well worth the attention of students even now:

For all but a small section of the population, education ended at the point where knowledge begins to exercise its fascination; and no small part of that section which had larger opportunities was chosen less on the ground of natural ability than of parental income. . . It was difficult. . .for the ordinary observer to believe that fifty per cent of the natural diplomatic talent in Great Britain was sent by a mysterious dispensation of Providence to the single school of Eton.

And from the same source:

> Neither the meaning of great literature nor the meaning of
> scientific discovery penetrated far beyond a small elite in society.
> Yet without their creative influence a large part of the quality of
> civilisation had little or no meaning for most citizens. Anyone
> who thinks of the small part played by books in the household of
> an average Englishman even of comfortable means must realise
> how many of the gates of civilisation were closed to them.

These remarks apply, as we see, to the British region; but the same
could be said of most of the Western world then. What is more difficult
for us to determine at this space of time is why the socio-moral position
was not better in the area of the Eastern Bloc, having regard to the fact
that serious attention was paid to education there, even including world
literature up to a point. There, too, all the limitations of ancient
education applied: its artificiality, misconceptions and so on. For all
that, it was fairly well diffused among the people and could have been
expected to have moderately good results. Yet, in spite of the socialistic
type of regime, government-run in the public interest to all intents and
purposes, juvenile delinquency, lack of social responsibility and
materialist outlook were rampant, if less than in the West. It is generally
considered nowadays that although education was not so inadequate,
its good effects were nullified by that very governmental rule which
made the people feel themselves helpless puppets and deprived them of
any sense of worthwhileness in working for the public good. The
Westerners undoubtedly felt themselves masters of their own
fates — and rarely realized that they were but doped dupes, neatly
insensitized by that fearful advertising, along with plenty of carefully
disguised governmental propaganda too: the political myth in action
*in excelsis.*
And insensitized they indeed were; insensitized to the claims of
humanity itself. We return to Harold Laski:

> ... the material inequalities we permit, the difference in the
> health, the housing, the nutrition, the power to travel, of the rich
> and the poor. A society is intelligible enough which makes some
> differentiation in reward in terms of the social functions its
> members perform; in any ethical terms, it is difficult to regard a
> society as rational in which the response to want is proportionate

to skill in the exploitation of an acquisitive impulse unrelated to social need. The adulation which is heaped upon wealth, the incredible elements which go to the making of social prestige, the transformation of charity into an organised profession, the relation of what Veblen called "conspicuous waste" to esteem, the fact that "a great Churchman" means, not a great Christian, but an important ecclesiastic, the persistence of the belief that the manual vocations are, in some mysterious way, less dignified than the clerical, all these indicate, in their different ways, a society which is sick at its foundations. . .

The last complaint in the list reminds one of that almost incredible willingness to give the world's dirty work permanently to a set of people called the lower classes and another set called natives or undeveloped peoples (together they formed most of the world's population). In the worst phase – and it only partially passed as the century advanced – these countless unfortunates were deliberately made sub-human by denying cluture to them and directing their attention to base pleasures in a setting of intensively-advertised "freedom" and "human dignity" propaganda, so that they slaved away unknowingly for their taskmasters. What a difference from the modern world, where all our young people do their year of public service in cleaning, basic production, transport, etc., at the conclusion of their basic education, interlinked with slight additional studies, followed by a few short periods of further such public service in more suitably adult fields later in life! Admittedly, our science is so much advanced by now that we can do most things automatically, and the world's dirty work is but a fraction of what it was a millenium ago. But even in those days, automation was beginning and primary work was already but a fraction of what it was in very ancient times. Twentieth century men could also have spread the burden reasonably if they had wished: that is to say, the effective controllers of society could have done. But of course they did not wish anything of the sort. That is what we find so difficult to believe. It is quite true, though; the historical evidence is overwhelming.

In fact, the outstanding feature of the twentieth century was cruelty – and where violence was avoided, its expression was callousness. Although today we are just beginning to achieve the techniques of self-mastery, man is really a very terrible creature indeed. As the Nazis proved – those Nazis whose ghastly crimes will ever go echoing down the halls of history – there are no limits to his conscious cruelty. But even the ordinary people of those times were not exactly worth boasting about as a rule, if judged from a humanist standpoint. Far and away the most dreadful thing was not lack of intellectual grasp, gravely limited – even reprehensibly so – as this was, but lack of feeling. People would pass a slum without blinking, read of terrible motor accidents and wars without any internal, let alone external, comment. The sheer lack of imagination in the realm of fellow-feeling was frightful. Only a handful felt and understood – and published mostly unread pamphlets in shoals.

Appeals to public need, the sense of service to one's fellows, were mostly hopeless, as far as we can gather. Response was always minimal, it seems, and never enough to change the face of society. We cannot be certain, but the impression is gained that the twentieth century, with its world wars and its Nazis, its widespread car-driving power-lust and all the rest of it, reached depths rarely, if ever, touched in other centuries – in spite of all the Neros and Attilas and semi-savage hordes of very ancient times, to mention but a mere item or two amid the historical horrors which have accompanied man's progress. When, nowadays, we hold our memorial meetings every New Year's Day, to commemorate those who suffered in human history (not excluding the animals, man's companions on this planet, albeit lower in the evolutionary scale, to which, too, man often brought unnecessary misery) we do well to give that regrettable twentieth century a rather prominent place in our thoughts. This humanistic practice of ours indeed serves a helpful purpose in reminding us to maintain ourselves at high standards on the correct moral path.

Not only was this a cruel and callous, or at best an uncaring century, to an almost unwonted degree. It was also a very ugly one. With all too few outstanding exceptions, cities were commonly of repulsive ugliness and even filth. No visible responsibility to fellow-men was revealed in them. Although building licenses were often necessary, for the most part everyone could build as he liked to the limit of his wealth or loans! Naturally the result was totally inartistic confusion, only occasionally mitigated by definite architectural planning. Sometimes, but not so often as in previous centuries, a pervading style impressed itself on a district, as it were, and the results were passable. But most towns were a muddled mess, on top of which the sordid remains of squalid workers' housing of the preceding century were by no means entirely eradicated in the twentieth century at all. We can hardly imagine the hideous results today: the old pictures and films seem like nightmarish fabrications. But again — it was only too true. Naturally, all our streets and towns, villages and cities, are designed by artists today, this being, of course, the main social function of the artist-architect in our time. The Eastern Bloc did, in fact, start on the realization of this concept even back then, but apparently suffered from a dearth of imaginative artists. With rare, brilliant exceptions, the West produced architectural chaos in the name of freedom, once again demonstrating its unhappy adroitness in slipping from balanced freedom to thoughtless license. It would take us far too long to go into the position of art in the twentieth century; as in the case of education, we can only refer our readers to the many competent specialist studies on the subject. Sufficient to say here that quite generally in the Western world at that period there was no approach to art whatever; it was frequently not regarded as an integral part of life at all! There were no Art Departments in every place as now; and an experimental request for green and black clouds on a yellow sky, as one such Department received not long ago, could not have been either filed or filled, even if the technical requirements for carrying it out could have been met — which of course they certainly could not, so long ago.

Since we have long taught history chiefly by means of mass-produced plastic copies of newspapers of the past (in translation in the world language for elementary students), covering events in the phrasing of the day after their occurrence, much of the overall picture presented above will not ring absolutely strange in our readers' mental ears. It is the acceptance of the facts that is so difficult — their mental realization. It is utterly incomprehensible to us today that the essentials of life — food, clothes and housing — were sold privately and competitively. One does not play with such essentials. But apart from Welfare State or Eastern Bloc controls, they did. It is also apparent to us that paternal millionaire endowments and all other charity, apart from essential, personal, human service, are simply signs of a diseased society. An efficiently run society does not call for such risky, chance, individual care in any way. But twentieth century man still took such matters for granted, as natural occurrences, just as in previous centuries.

Goethe said the cultured man must know the culture of 3000 years. So, in the year 3000, we at least need to have some concept of what was going on in our world only one millenium ago. How balanced our mental picture can be is inevitably a moot point. The above account has been mainly doleful, for, as far as we can say now, that was the prevailing condition at that time. But it would be absurd to pretend that everything was bleak and black, that hopelessness and helplessness prevailed everywhere, that no life was worth living. That would undoubtedly be nonsense. There were fine things and fine lives in the twentieth century, as at all times in human history; not a few were very fine indeed. It would be appropriate to round off the present account in a tone of moderation. The region famous for the moderation of its people in our review period was the little British region of northwestern Europe, from which most of our quoted comments on the general scene have originated. Fulfilling our expressed intention to return to the rather unusual subject of Britain, we shall make it central in our social summing-up.

The British Islands, as they were then named, had had a turbulent history of oft-repeated invasion from different points of the adjacent European Continent; consequently they showed a remarkable muddle of cultures after several centuries of such mixed development added to the original stock, of which we know little. Little by little, matters settled down — as nowhere else in Europe — to a state of stabilized muddle. The local language, spread around the world by British martial qualities, was a muddle of various southern and northern sources; the British became famous for quite successfully muddling through more or less everything. They ran a relatively good parliamentary democracy, in which the parties were ever getting muddled up, superimposed on a basically feudal aristocracy which seemed to survive indefinitely from the time of a Norman invasion they once had. They were among the last exponents on earth of primitive god-king (or perhaps it was king-god) worship, their surviving newspapers showing them to regard their Royal Family, as it was carefully termed with capital letters, as sacred, to all intents and purposes.

In this strangely artificial atmosphere, most things achieved the acme of moderation and stayed there. There were indeed extremes of rich and poor, and even of beauty and ugliness, but these were exceptional: matters had to be kept more or less in the middle of the road, or the various contradictory elements in the general muddle would have torn the whole social structure apart. So the British became well-known for moderate and gentlemanly behavior, for fair-play — and for hypocrisy. That this latter failing was actually any worse than it was anywhere else is rather doubtful; but the pervading style of moderation must have made the British look particularly insincere in the eyes of less self-controlled peoples elsewhere, who simply could not believe that anyone could feel as detached as the British made themselves out to be.

It seems that the release for all this successful effort at utmost moderation came in the national sport of football and, for that matter, in all sport, which the British, above all, spread around the world. Here, not only was restraint unknown, but the topic basically dominated local life. Such are the childish whims which replace unfed fundamental strivings of the human spirit! Or such they were, rather, for we have long since outgrown such elementary follies. Certainly sport has a place in our world, essentially among youth, in that some types still do not find their natural field of physical development in long-distance tourist walking. But it is a minor matter, and it is no longer usual for other than children to play ball. The entire phenomenon of sport on a vast scale (almost entirely vicarious) in the twentieth century world is even now worth additional study; it so clearly expressed the non-satisfaction of yearnings for self-fulfilment which that crude, soulless age brought about.

Yet, with all this, the British region had produced probably the finest literature in the world in previous centuries, no doubt on account of the unusually broad mixture of genes concentrated in such a small area. In the twentieth century itself, it also produced some of the best music of the period. Even today, although long since incorporated in the European branch of civilization, certain specific characteristics prevail in and around the British region of old: perhaps rather more emphasis on sport than prevails on the average elsewhere, and quite certainly some little remainder, at least, of that rather grand old moderation in personal character. We can often trace back local characteristics of all sorts to previous regional history; but the British example is particularly typical, and we have chosen it here as a prominent specimen of mingled good and bad in the civilization of a thousand years ago.

It is appropriate here to insert one more British quotation, as typical of some of the best of that quaint old place. It is by the contemporary writer, J. B. Priestley, in a book called *Rain upon Godshill* (Godshill, his home, was on an island to the south of the main British island as it was then):

> We cannot get our values and our cosmology right because we can no longer think quietly and creatively; we can no longer think quietly and creatively because we now live in a world of alarms and crises; we now live in a world of alarms and crises because we have thrown over any idea of universal trust and cooperation; we

have thrown over any idea of universal trust and cooperation because we no longer hold beliefs that tend to unify us; and we no longer hold beliefs that tend to unify us because we cannot get our values and cosmology right. Let us admit the truth.

Not an all-encompassing statement, but a fine expression of the vicious circle in which the declining civilization of the twentieth century was caught.

For all that, we want to be fair even to that tormented old declining civilization. To show it at its best we turn to its grand philosopher, Albert Schweitzer, for a concluding quotation to our review of the general social position then prevailing. This outstanding philosopher had developed the concept of reverence for life, parallelling an aspect of ancient Buddhism, and he explained a part of it thus:

> The concept of Reverence for Life does not allow the scholar to live for science alone, even if he is very useful to the community in so doing. It does not permit the artist to exist only for his art, even if it gives inspiration to many by its means. It refuses to let the businessman imagine that he fulfils all legitimate demands in the course of his business activity. It demands from all that they should sacrifice a portion of their own lives for others.

What is a commonplace of universal acceptance on our part today was a daringly advanced thought to proffer a millenium ago. But in such an example, we can see how the flame of pure humanity, which had begun to glow in very ancient times, only to flicker badly in the worst of subsequent ages, never went out altogether. The line is continuous; and it is only right to recognize that some of the aspects of our own sane society are descended from the all-too-overshadowed better elements in even that unlucky civilization we have attempted to survey socially.

# 2 The Scientific Position

When we turn to science, prowess in which so directly determines the shape of society, we again find our twentieth century holding a special place in history. Building on the foundations of the previous century above all, when the breakthrough to relative modernity and wholesale industrialization had started, it was this century which first saw electronics in numerous manifestations, computers, and automated production. This can truly be said to be the time when the modern scientific world began its development.

But — and perhaps this was not really surprising at such an early stage — the whole scientific structure and outlook of the age was inadequately based. Precisely this fact may well have had a good deal to do with the socio-moral inadequacies of the time already stressed. The connection should become obvious by the end of this exposition of the scientific position.

The matter can be expressed very simply in essence. Although something was known of electricity, radiation, and energy (effectually synonymous terms, but this was not realized then), science restricted itself almost entirely to their physical and chemical manifestations. This was especially true of biochemistry, particularly ludicrous though it was in the field of life, which is above all a complex of electrical currents and fields, literally speaking. Admittedly, brain and nerve electricity had been recognized even before the middle of the twentieth century, and no little attention was paid to them during its second half. Yet this was almost a detached study, a relatively unimportant branch of physiology; so far as we can judge, no serious attempt whatever was made at a link-up between the energy of the universe and the life-currents of animate beings in it.

Worse still, there was apparently no realization whatever that there is

no such thing as a chemical reaction without a current-flow. For
instance, all they had managed to find out in those days was that water
was composed of oxygen and hydrogen. It seems that it never even
occurred to them to seek after the electrical energy transmission which
alone makes such fusion of elements possible. They did not even realize
that the elements are no more and no less than crystallized energy in
graduated forms. They had indeed been struck by the fundamental
significance of crystallization in nature, and had even seen the parallel
between the growth-forms of some crystals and those of some plants.
But the current-flow determining such forms, in fact linking non-life
with life — basically that same universal energy, but intensified on the
life side of the bridge and thus amounting actually to life instead of
being only its potentiality — that current-flow, the literally vital basis of
the whole proceeding, escaped them! We do know of one outstanding
book, which has come down to us, Charles Sherrington's *Man on his
Nature,* which gets rather near to these matters by implication. There
are occasional other hints here and there in the writing of the time. But
they are the merest gropings, the barest suggestions, never followed
through to definite conclusions, scarcely even hints, in fact. They were
on the brink, and never knew it! We cannot help feeling disappointed in
twentieth century scientists that they never quite made the really big
breakthrough, in spite of their fairly successful nuclear physics and
other achievements. Only in subsequent centuries was the basic gap to
be filled.

However, in one case, and one case only, as far as the records have
come down to us, the gap was virtually filled in a priliminary, a quasi-,
a pseudo-, an almost visionary way. Two other contemporary books
were mentioned in connection with this rather visionary presentation,
and we shall reproduce the mentions along with the presentation itself, but one is far from the essence of the matter, and the other, if
admittedly nearer, is still by no means the same thing.

The actual presentation occurs almost at the beginning of a very
peculiar book indeed. This was a book mostly devoted to Zionism, the
national philosophy of the Jewish people of that period. At the
beginning, though, it is very general in character, apparently setting the
world-stage on which the Jewish people afterwards appear. Unfortunately, it is one of many examples which have come down to us from
the twentieth century in an incomplete state: that is to say, without
cover and title-page. Not only was the bookbinding of that period
atrociously weak, but, owing to the poverty of the age in general, they

produced many (if not most) of their books with merely paper covers. In such circumstances, it is not surprising that archaeologists have ever since been digging up damaged books of the time, the damage most frequently consisting of missing covers and first and last pages – obviously particularly exasperating to researchers. The present example has no more than the cover and title-page missing; but that is enough to leave us completely in the dark as to its origin. Only one copy has ever been found, and that in the Chinese region, of all places. It has no connection whatever with that region, obviously belonging to Europe or West Asia; it must have been taken there by some traveller. The surprising nature of its contents has made it fairly well known among students of its period, but so far as we can ascertain, extracts from it have never been made available to the general public. We believe we are performing a specially valuable service in bringing some of its most interesting pages before a wide range of readers in the present publication.

The first relevant section is entitled, "The place of personality in a universe of radiation."

Those who are familiar with the best of our century's literature on man's place in the universe will realise at once that we have changed three words in the title of an extremely significant book by Wolfgang Köhler (*The Place of Value in a World of Facts*) and thus adapted his euphonious wording to our own purposes in this introductory stage of our argument. We should like, at one and the same time, to apologise for such clumsy "borrowing" and to mention that it is our poor way of paying tribute to the author of a contribution of rare importance towards answering the vexed question of what we are supposed to be doing here – or, if preferred, of what we are supposed to be being.

It is no part of our present business to attempt to summarise the brilliant work of Köhler as a synthesis of physics and psychology resulting in philosophy – if, in fact, it is at all permissible to describe his work in this way, which it probably is not. But at the risk – nay, the virtual certainty – of unforgivable distortion, we cannot avoid stating the thoughts that his work aroused. Even if they are not really implied by him himself, the matter is extremely relevant to our own aims.

We might say, building on his much more precise and cautious

thesis, that, owing to the electrical field forces in the brain, we
sense a need for balance when we witness anything unbalanced.
Anything unfinished or discontinuous causes, as it were, an excess
voltage on one side of the brain. This constitutes a phenomenon
of "requiredness," demanding the necessary voltage adjustment
on the other side, in order to restore the balance. It is this
requiredness which is the basis for human values, they being an
expression, therefore, of minute voltage differences in the brain's
electrical field. A kink in a curve, taken to the brain through the
mechanism of the eye, immediately induces, by electrical means,
the desire to straighten out the kink so as to restore the curve
unsullied.

It is, of course, rather a long jump from our suggested picture
of this kind, based on a sort of mechanical requiredness, to the
whole structure of human values, and Köhler certainly does not
intend to carry his theory so far, mentioning only once, in
passing, its possible development in this direction. But if he
restricted himself to laying the foundations, he truly opens up
new vistas of thought, as implied in his compelling title, and
entirely on our own responsibility, we are inclined to develop
them a little.

Being foolish enough to rush in where angels fear to tread, we
wish to present a certain hypothesis, as basis for a consideration
of a specific aspect of human endeavour. We formulated this
before having the pleasure of reading Köhler's notable work, but
as far as we know it does not clash with it in any but one or two
tiny details which in any case do not concern us here. It is natural
that we too should think in electrical terms, for there are hardly
any others worth thinking in nowadays. However, instead of
chemically induced currents, our own thought runs rather on the
lines of radio, without in the least suggesting that the induced
currents are not there, for many of them, at any rate, certainly
are.

We need to explain ourselves at the outset by stating quite
frankly that we are postulating something which is, as yet,
outside the bounds of all possibility of proof, for there is, as yet,
no means of measuring such ultra-microscopic electrical waves as
are involved in our suggestion. The position is, in fact, still worse
than this, for it is quite conceivable that we may never be able to
measure such waves at all. If we ever succeed in developing such

delicate measuring instruments as can detect them, it is perfectly possible that the very action of measurement will deflect them, and we shall arrive back again at the indeterminacy principle which prevents us from determining the exact position of the smallest particles because as soon as we approach we unavoidably push them out of the way into some other position.

It is agreed that there is a certain emission of electrical waves from the brain, but it has been found that they cannot be detected at distances greater than a few millimeters. Electricity of this very limited transmission range may be quite sufficient for Professor Köhler's purposes, but it will be totally inadequate for ours. As soon as we begin to catalog the problems still demanding a physical explanation, which we have in mind, it will be seen why. We would emphasise that we are not necessarily asking for too much. There really are various kinds of electricity, and there is no reason why there should not be one kind more – or several – which we have not yet been able to identify. Magnetism is different from electricity generated in a power station. Short radio waves are different from long ones. Should we consider light waves as a form of electricity? And what cf cosmic radiation? Clearly we are not speaking in any precisely defined terms and can be held guilty of mixing matters grossly brusquely. But, in a sense, this is nearer our actual intention than sharp categorisation would be. For in the last resort, is not everything resolvable into electrons, protons, neutrons of some sort? In other words, is not everything electricity in some form?

Although considerably increased attention has been directed in recent years to the phenomenon of extrasensory perception (ESP or psi), it can hardly be said to be taken very much into account in general. Yet telepathy, clairvoyance and even precognition have long been accurately reported and scientifically checked on a large scale. Perhaps the most significant experiment of very many was one in which very gently rolling balls were apparently deflected to one side or the other of their chute by sheer concentrated will-power. The mathematical laws of chance were statistically determined to be entirely out of operation in relation to the remarkable results obtained. No scientific explanation has yet been given for numerous adequately checked examples of the peculiar mental influence of so-called witch-doctors and similar practitioners in Tibet, Polynesia, various regions of Africa and so

on. By no means all such phenomena can be explained by
first-class conjuring technique, although it is known that much of
it can. Spiritualism is undeniably in much weaker case, but a great
deal of ghost and poltergeist material is still awaiting explanation.
One of various fire-walking performances in the East, in which
neither feet nor stockings showed the slightest signs of burning
evoked from observing scientists the frank suggestion that there
must have been some sort of psychological waves emitted by the
ecstatically worshipping participants which overcame the normal
effects of fire upon them. Perhaps we may be permitted to take
our cue from this and to develop the concept of "psychological
waves" very much further.

If we postulate the existence of direct mental power over
matter without intervening mechanical means, we are forced to
suggest that the intervention is done electrically by some kind of
ultra-micro-radio waves, which will have properties different from
those of any of the various other kinds of electrical radiation we
listed in the penultimate paragraph, all of which themselves have
different properties as concerns distance of penetration, for
instance. As soon, however, as we make a suggestion like this, we
find that we may have to reconstitute our everyday picture of the
universe to a basic degree. Man has been in the habit of making a
clear-cut distinction between mind and matter throughout
history, and this distinction has been at the root of most schools
of philosophy. If, though, we make a quasi-radio connection
between mind and matter, do we not go a long way towards
breaking down the opposition between the spiritual and the
material altogether, with the possibility of breaking it down
entirely in the end?

We should surely feel happier (in Köhlerian phraseology, the
voltage-differential in our brains would be smoothed out) if we
could do away with the troublesome thought that there are two
kinds of stuff in the universe, material and immaterial, mind
having apparently evolved from matter as higher forms of life
emerged, without there being any particular reason for even life,
let alone mind, to come about at all. If we see both mind and
matter as emanations of the radiation released from the primeval
atom (or, in continuous-creation terms, as radiational emanations
from the constantly introjected hydrogen), the phenomenon of
man and of other beings in the universe suddenly falls into place

considerably more easily than before. Man is no longer a strange manifestation of inexplicable life evolved from whirling masses of inert matter. He is simply an even more vivid radiation-product than anything else, but he is intimately connected by radiational means with everything else. His radiating mind is a kind of transmuted and re-caught-up speck of the original universe-radiation.

We must make it clear here that we do not wish to be taken too literally: we were speaking somewhat metaphorically in our last sentence, which, however, we think justified by reason of its presenting an inclusive vista. It is obvious that the original radiational material (there is not even any great point in making a distinction between radiation and material in the last resort, although it is certainly useful to do so in daily life!) cooled down and crystallised into, among other things, amino-acids from which life emerged, taking on the forms of an enormous variety of physical bodies. So if life is essentially a kind of radiation, it is a secondary radiation, evolved through physical bodies. But this is not to say that it is disconnected from the primary radiation of the universe, for the physical bodies and indeed all material are themselves crystallised radiation, if we may phrase matters in so unorthodox a manner. The story of the universe is a story of radiation. Then, if we may legitimately postulate that molecular attraction is electrical (radiational) in essence, we need surely have no difficulty in seeing the primeval radiation pervading all matter, forming the basis of its crystallisation, and afterwards working itself out quite inevitably in the various forms of life (based on a vast range of frequencies, in complex combinations), and finally expressing itself in the mind of man, a necessary emanation from living entities of highly developed functions.

It is a curious thing that for something like a century the new science of psychology has built itself up on no material basis whatever. That is to say, no direct connection has ever been found between mind and body. We know quite well by now that certain actions cause certain psychological reactions and so on, but we have never been able to catch hold of a thought, as one might say, and describe exactly how the thought itself sends electrical currents off through the brain to actuate certain nerve centers and so get the required muscles moved; nor how a thought of fear or anger influences a gland to excrete more or less of an appropriate chemical substance. But if we describe the thought as a tiny transmission of radiation, we can go on to imagine a radio connection with the electricity of the body and thus establish the missing link of direct mind-body interaction.

Now it becomes possible to understand "miraculous" restorations of diseased bodies to health: radiation of suitable wavelength from the brain tones up the damaged electrical system of the body and enables physical repair process to be carried out successfully. There is no need to restrict the process to an individual internally. The apparent irradiation of health by, say, a devoted mother, into a sick child can also be explained in the same way, as can telepathy in general, and much more besides. For example, the apparently strange killing of enemies in the jungle at a distance by incantations and curses may well be the result of projection, a beamed broadcast of personal radiation on a wavelength which jams the enemy's own and, by means of such electrical mental influence over the body, brings its physical working to a standstill (typified in practice by mental depression and physical illness without evident cause). Hypnotism, too, can be explained on similar lines as a milder jamming of the hypnotised person's electrical mentality.

We can go much further still, and attempt to attack the problem of personality. It has been legitimately complained that science has never yet really come to grips with man as man. The most compelling question of all in this field — what constitutes each individual human personality? — has never been scientifically tackled. It has been walked around, psychologically or perhaps biochemically, but no actual synthesis has been attempted. Let us suggest, then, by way of hypothesis, that a living body constitutes a kind of transmitting, as well as a receiving, station of radiation, and that its highest evolved type, the human body, has a kind of radiated aura around it which can be "instinctively felt" as a definite personality. We can, then, visualise the human being as a sort of broadcasting station, the body being the chemical apparatus which generates the electricity through its biochemistry, just as an electric accumulator does from its plates. The mind may be considered as the directing control-panel. When the personality-aura is beamed to a person on a suitable wavelength, the various ESP effects we have mentioned take place, such telepathetic transmission evidently being superior to any ordinary radio transmission that we know, since distance and "atmospheric" disturbances of an electrical nature seem to be no obstacles. The fact that such "beaming" often leaves the "transmitting" person physically exhausted lends some material support to the view that we may not be conjecturing unduly theoretically. We can adduce further support from such phenomena as that of "feeling" sómeone is looking at us although we do not see them and have no reason to suppose anyone is doing anything of the sort; and turning round to find that someone is indeed looking at us. If this is not the result of personal radiation being projected upon us, of what is it the result?

The human personality has the remarkable power of interacting with other personalities by way of emotional reaction. This transcends the interpenetration of minds, for instance, so that we are, perhaps "against ourselves" attracted to or repelled from other personalities without ever "knowing" these others in a knowledgeable sense at all. A strong human personality, too, can influence multitudes, not by mere psychological showmanship, but by what we call "force of character," which may be something much quieter than great intellectual power (the charismatic personality). When we speak of "a magnetic personality," we may be literally nearer to the scientific truth of the matter than we know. Attraction and repulsion between personality-auras, according to the tunability or untunability of their radiation wavelengths, might give a better explanation of love and hate than the psychologists have yet managed to provide. Moreover, we might suggest in passing that the basis of sex might be even more electrical than chemical and that it might be as fundamental in the universe as what we call positive and negative charges of electricity, being, in fact, just that.

By viewing an individual's personality-aura as an evolved unit, we might be going behind psychology to something much more fundamental still, visualising an inclusive envelope, as it were, containing body and mind in its biochemically generated radiation system. This will thus constitute the amalgam of thoughts and feelings which add up to that wondrous subjective-objective creature, the individual man. For, in this view, we no longer have any reason to separate thoughts and feelings into different compartments and to regard the former as high-level intellectual productions (or, of course, as low-level semi- or sub-conscious ones, as the case may be), while the latter are looked down upon as merely primitive instinctual manifestations. Feelings, too, may now be seen as perfectly legitimate radiation effects in their own right. While we should not wish to exaggerate the possible significance of intuition as Bergson is sometimes accused of doing, we could at least refrain from unwisely going the whole rationalist hog. It would be better to suggest that the future of mankind does not necessarily depend upon the perfection of reason alone, although we certainly do not wish to detract one whit from the profound importance of reason.

The individual always seems to have had an insistent internal urge to express himself. Art, culture, in a word, civilization itself (basically intellectual on its organizational side, but partly emotional too) has come about. It is as though man's personality-aura radiation could not help transmitting. Of course it could not, for it is life itself, issued from the primary radiation of the universe. And if transmitting also receiving; all the time interaction on tunable wavelengths is taking place. The commonest wavelengths would constitute standards; so aesthetic taste could be crystallised and culturally transmitted by educational means afterwards through the generations. In this way, we can find a place for artistic culture in the very structure of the universe. Nothing less is required, as a matter of fact, from any logical standpoint. To leave art floating about in mid-air on its own, as one might say, without any connection with the rest of creation, must always seem unsatisfactory, for it causes us a Köhlerian electro-mental imbalance, as does any unsolved problem. No doubt most of the basis of art can be explained quite well as a gamut of electrical tensions and releases in the brain. Still, we hope it may be feasible to add a little of our wavelength-theorising to Köhler's soundly based psycho-physical presentation, in order to explain why an artist chooses to paint in this color or that, this form or that, and so on, and so, similarly, with drama, architecture, music and the other arts. He surely chooses manifestations of light and sound wavelengths which are amenable to the intrinsic wavelengths of his own physico-mentality, possibly mathematical harmonics of them, or tunable wavelengths anyway. Most likely, the greatest art of the greatest artists vibrates on fundamental frequencies of the universe energy.

If this is the case with art, representing one aspect of personality, it may surely be no less so with other aspects, and not least the moral one. The moral ideal can be the naturally most stable (therefore satisfying) set of radiation-wavelengths to balance the voltages on the two sides of the brain. This suggests some intuitive reality to the religious claim that righteousness, etc. (ideals) are "ordained" in the universe, for they are indeed thus implicit in its electrical structure as manifested in human life. Evil "ideals" cannot supply such a balance, for they leave unsatisfied the inter-radiatory feeling for the equal interests of others. The fact is that we do not know or understand what is going on in the field of our desires (long-term ideals, especially).

At any rate, Erich Fromm stressed in *Man for Himself* that there are two sorts of conscience in the individual: what we may briefly refer to as the Freudian one, due to the largely unavoidable authoritarianism of our parents, and what he terms the humanistic one, which expresses our inmost being – the true voice of ourselves within ourselves. (We shall have occasion later to add the "social conscience" of Durkheim to these two, and so make a triple Freud-Fromm-Durkheim compound in order to present the social individual adequately, but we are not concerned with this additional complication for the moment.) Dissatisfied as we have already expressed ourselves with a purely psychological explanation of psychology, which seems to us little more than gratuitous scientific mysticism, we are clearly ready to claim that this true voice of ourselves within ourselves may in fact be the expression of our basic physico-electrical wavelengths. If an internal radio connection is postulated within the pattern of the brain's electrical field, itself significantly moulded by our early relationship with our parents, we can thus make a link between Freudian and Frommian conscience, and later add Durkheimian conscience. This latter doubtless evolved through influences derived from experience which affected the brain's electrical field-structure, much as the Freudian class of influences did. And since every type of conscience has an appropriate type of morality associated with it, by way of its practical expression, we are thus faced with Freudian morality, largely, but by no means entirely, sexual; with social morality; and, most important in our present context, with what we may call pure morality, born of the pure self, the intimate personality.

In this way, we have perhaps managed to find a place for morality in the universe in its own right, not as a mere fiction, however necessary, of man's imagination, but as a definite product of the original radiation of the universe in its evolution.

We have just mentioned the word "imagination" without making any comment alongside it or attempting any definition. It may be that there are some difficulties involved which can hardly be said to fall within our province of investigation, but, restricting ourselves to quite general terms, we would suggest that imagination can be fairly well explained as the product of the free play of electrical forces in our brains. We are by no means satisfied that our nutshell explanation is anything like complete; and we should certainly like to add an interplay of personality-wavelengths to it. The whole concept of "play" is probably basic to life; and here again, we cannot think of any explanation divorced from considerations of minute electrical voltages. Imagination is itself a very ambiguous term, in any case; in connecting it with the idea of play, we have implied that side of it which is particularly relevant to art, that of free fantasia. Social imagination, however, and other kinds, is a different matter. It implies thinking forward, teleology. But this too we would delimit electrically, this time within the framework of basic personality-wavelengths, for the moment leaving matters a little tentatively at that.

The more we pursue our general line of thought on the radiational basis of the universe and naturally of ourselves produced within it, the more present problems of science we find it possible to suggest as falling within its scope. It is conceivable, for example, that the physical death of the human body can leave the radiation from the personality-aura persisting for some time and so give rise to ghost phenomena when other personalities on a tunable wavelength come within range. This persistent personality radiation might even become enshrined within the radiation that may well be suspected to lurk within inanimate things too, albeit at much lesser strength. (To this suggestion we shall return very soon.) If so, the "ghost" might become attached to a certain place for indefinite periods, or manifest itself in poltergeist effects. (We realise that the electrical radiations with which we are familiar do not, in practice, persist for long; but we would stress that we are throughout postulating a kind of electricity which, as yet, we do not know in the least.)

Let us proceed. The rather indefinable mental contact between men and some animals, which reaches rare intimacy in the case of dogs in particular, strongly hinting at a certain degree of similarity of electrical brain structure (although we cannot possibly say why this should have occurred in evolution), suggests just the same sort of tuned radiation-interaction as we found suitable for explaining interaction between human personalities without the intervention of intellectual knowledge. In this context, we could take into account also the seemingly strange manner in which some people have power over animals and by beaming their will on them, as we might say, overcome their ferocity, as is related in sometimes well-authenticated traveller's tales. Bandits and other savages have also been known to be quelled by what is described as the faith of a missionary, for instance. If we do not wish to leave all mysticism as pure mystery in the realm of the imagination, which we dealt with perhaps too cavalierly and even a little scathingly above, what alternative have we but to apply some such electric-radiation hypothesis as ours to it? In the end, all the vague hints of the mystics must either come under scientific investigation and classification, or die a natural death as outmoded superstitions.

We cannot call a halt at the stage of the higher animals. Let us attribute to the lower animals too, to the fishes and insects, to all living creatures including plants, some feeble share of radiation — for what else is their life? Let us continue down the scale to the amoebas, jump through the amino-acids and come to inanimate matter. Should not our universal micro-electrical radiation be present in all of these in appropriately lesser degree? At some critical point in the quantity or intensity of it, may we not expect to find the border between life and non-life, with the viruses sitting right by that border, for instance? We are now in imagination (whether this be a product of dubious credentials or not!) approaching the realm of the heavier elements. They are radio-active. A variant of our hypothetical radiation, perhaps? But why stop? We need to subsume everything without exception in one inclusive, universal whole. Onwards then! — downwards in the scale of evolution. Why should we assume that only the heavy elements are radio-active? Why should not all, without exception, of the elements be radio-active, but in an impossible-to-measure degree? In fact, has not the fact been as good as admitted these many years, since it was found that matter invariably analyses down into what looks queerly like un-matter, just waves and radiation? (We shall not trouble to differentiate clearly between them, as they can be but two aspects of the same thing, and it is for mathematicians only to be precise in such matters. We have alluded throughout to "wavelengths," but, of course, we could equally have referred to "frequencies" for that matter, refraining only because it is a less familiar concept to all but modern radio enthusiasts.) Waves and radiation, then, here, there, and everywhere — the stars, our planet and ourselves, all made inevitably of the same stuff, waves of and in radiation (to be a little more precise at the last, for all that!), finding expression of human-individual nature in our personality-auras.

In this immeasurably sub-micro-electricity we have been postulating, this persistently broadcasting personal radiation emitted by our bodies, and its lesser counterparts emitted by everything else, we have, in effect, suggested an approach to the problem of revealing the essence of what constitutes life itself, as though it was just a matter of a tiny speck of additional voltage. And who knows? — so perhaps it may be.

True, we are no nearer to tackling the actual problem of creation; but, naturally, we never had any chance of doing so. We can, if we like, postulate a radiatory source for all the radiation; but to do so is merely to start pushing back the problem indefinitely. If, on the other hand, we choose to view the radiation as self-creative, we shall simultaneously be incorporating ourselves in this self-creativeness. This is quite in accord with recent ideas about man as partner in creation, but how far this partner is free to act is another question, which we must now investigate as well as may be.

And here, our unknown author from somewhere around the middle of the twentieth century, launches forth afresh, calling his next section, "Free will versus determinism again." In this, he seems somewhat less sure of himself, but within limits, his vision and grasp hold firm, and we feel sure our readers will retain their astonishment that anyone in ancient times could guess at even as partially close an approximation to our modern outlook as this:

Current   science,   in   finding   more   and   more   physical explanations for natural phenomena, leads to a more and more deterministic outlook. We ourselves, by almost equating mind with matter, or, rather more exactly, by seeking to break down the distinction between them by assuming both to be manifestations of the universe's original radiation in diversely developed forms, are obviously completely in line with this tendency. Before doing anything to abate the impression we have surely given of adhering to complete determinism, we should, in fact, even like to accentuate it still further.

From the picture we have given of the universe, it is difficult to find any room for chance or accident, let alone free will, to exist. Radiation being given, either in the first place or all the time, its subsequent development is implicit within it. Long before life appeared (in spite of being implicit from the outset), our universe evolved certain nebulae, galaxies, and all the rest of it, in a certain way resulting from the forces of the original radiation and gases it gave rise to. No other way was possible, or it would have occurred. It is true that other ways, based on other forces, were and are possible in other universes, and we have no method of ruling out the existence of such universes, since we can apparently have no possibility of knowing one way or the other. But in our own universe as we do know it, what was, was inevitable. If something else could have happened, why did it not? Consequently, it would seem that what is, is also inevitable, since what is, will later on be what was. The eruption of life into our universe at a later stage of development when the radiation had already crystallised into discrete physical entities, later becoming the secondary radiation which, we suggested, may constitute our personalities, has no need to make the slightest difference. Life and mind are simply later forms of the basic radiation and therefore necessarily take on the characteristics implicit in it from the start. What justification can there be for man to assume that he, merely yet another manifestation of the original forces, has received a special dispensation to get to grips with the universe on his own account and do what he likes with it as far as his powers extend? Even if we turn matters, as usually accepted, upside-down, and say, as our hypothesis permits us to say, that mind, being itself a form of radiation, is primary in the universe, and not matter (which could be regarded as a mere vehicle for the primary radiation to become transformed into our secondary radiation) – we shall still be no better off. (We shall not stop to differentiate precisely between mind and personality, which are in any case, inextricably bound together. Probably personality, in a way, could be regarded as static, and mind as the dynamic aspect of it.) All radiation products evolve and function according to their intrinsic propensities; men, microbes, mind, material – it makes no difference.

Wriggle as we may, there seems to be no loophole. It appears that the course of evolution of living things has been largely, if not essentially, determined by mutations of genes. We still do not know for sure whether these mutations are caused by the impact of cosmic radiation or not, but the theory obviously seems amenable to our point of view as expressed above. But whether this or any other cause is the responsible one, there is no need to bring in the element of chance. A gene is found in a certain position; a cosmic ray or other influence impacts with it at a certain strength and at a certain angle and the mutation takes place. Presumably this is another example of the intimate connection between electricity and biochemistry: in fact, one might almost as well speak only of bioelectricity, the chemistry being in any case taken for granted as being included in the "bio-." The gene, the ray, everything has evolved through natural forces and turns up, at any given moment, where it turns up, and that is that.

The whole procedure can be transferred without change to the human sphere. One man meets another, being brought to the place by a vast multiplicity of miscellaneous causes extending infinitely backwards into history, pre-history and the remotest times; they interact positively or negatively according to the various complex forces with which they have been endowed and according to the infinitude of circumstances surrounding them at the time and throughout their personal pasts; and, again, that is that. No actual place for chance seems evident, nor any place for free will to be exercised. If human values and consequent actions, aesthetic taste and all the other manifestations of personality, are bioelectrical excretions, consequent upon particular voltages and wavelengths, it is evidently necessary to change the meaning of the word "spiritual" in a very material manner.

We have gone so far as to suggest that mind may be even more fundamental in the universe than matter; but we do so very diffidently, for the potential implications are serious. It is not so much that the idea seems to be an outrageously proud one, attributing altogether colossally absurd importance to ourselves, although we are so insignificant in a vast universe of whirling galaxies that we can barely call ourselves even specks. For one thing, as many philosophers have previously pointed out, quality may genuinely be much more significant than quantity, for the simple reason that evolution appears to be going in a definite direction, and that direction is one of higher and higher quality in the sense of functional scope and sensitivity. For another thing, there is really no justification whatever to assume that we are the sole inhabitants of the universe, nor even of our own corner of it. If life has developed on our planet, it can have developed on myriads. In due course, we shall naturally meet our distant contemporaries, although how we shall be able to communicate with them if they are in various cases quite a few million, or even a few thousand, years ahead of us in evolution, is yet another pretty problem. A whole vast new phase of human, and perhaps super human, activity lies out ahead there in the as yet unknown dark spaces of the future. Fortunately, it is not any part of our business to sketch such possibilities, but the passing mention of them reminds us that they have, in effect, long since been superbly visualised by Olaf Stapledon in his *Last and First Men,* a classic forerunner of the comparatively petty science fiction of today.

The point is that, in one way or another, there is at least a possibility that our universe is geared to life of a high order — that is to say that the character of its basic radiation is such that mind of human type is, if not its end-product, an inevitable stage in the progress towards the end-product, whatever the latter may be. To us, the overwhelmingly tremendous forces employed for the eventual production of human, and probably other, mentality seem fantastically wasteful. But then we are used to doing things on a tiny scale on our little planet, so we are really not possessed of a suitable scale of appraisal. Life and mind are not really little things. They may even be so big that unimaginable quantities of electrified materials dotted about in an indescribably vast universe may not be unduly expensive as a means of producing them. However, we are unlikely ever to become adept as cosmic economics, so we shall leave this unworkable subject at this point – with the addition of an admission that we may, for all that, have been unconsciously exaggerating in the opposite direction. It is not entirely impossible that life and mind are merely insignificant by-products and that the flaming masses of gas and so on are really the central features of the universe. But, on the whole, we think the course of evolution as we know it so far rather strongly suggests the opposite, and that the latter view is less tenable than our preceding one.

Even so, it is far from clear that we are in any better case. However important in the scheme of things life and human life may be, we may still well be the slaves of the life-force, of the radiation-source's rays. It is true that man may be considered not only as an animal come to consciousness (in the sense, of course, of self-consciousness) in the process of evolution; he may even be considered as evolution itself comes to consciousness. More, why should he not look on himself as the very universe come to consciousness? Yet consciousness does not, of itself, imply free will. There is no logical connection between the two.

What it presumably does imply is a feeling of free will, but only a feeling of it. It is this awkward point that may have been leading some of us astray for millenia. In order that a unitary mind should become actual, it must needs be enshrined in a definite organism – in a physical body. Otherwise, it cannot develop the characteristics, the powers of conception, which alone enable us to define it as a mind. Now a mind in a physical body is surely bound to bear within itself the impression that it has freedom of action, or it could not act at all; the body would not move, life could not go on in the human sense. Bergson explained the genesis of the mind as the outcome of a body faced with various possibilities of movement (and we can almost define life as self-movement); intelligence is born of indecision. So far, so good. But we have still not broken through to free will. What we have arrived at is indecision. The indecision, however, is resolved, one way or another, not at all necessarily by the truly free thought of the individual, but by the final balance of the innumerable hereditary and environmental forces playing on his brain – radiational forces playing on a radiational brain, affecting its internal voltages and so bringing about the ultimate decision "chosen." It all seems a game – a trick evolved nature is forever playing on us, bringing us to unavoidable self-delusion, self-deception.

If it seems strange that we should be discussing free will without having made any previous reference to will as such, free or not, we may clarify our position somewhat at this point by stating openly what we have implied all along: that we see no need to confuse matters by regarding mind and will as separate entities, as has sometimes been done in the past. For us, will is an aspect of part of the mind itself, that part which is "beamed" or directed to a specific purpose. Will, like the rest of mind, is, in accordance with our previous hypothesis, an aspect of the intrinsic self, Fromm's intimate humanistic conscience, our "personality" with its aura. When we consider free will, therefore, we are not considering any addition to a human being, tacked on to him, as it were, which he can manipulate or not; we are considering the essence of the human being himself.

Having done our best to dash all hopes of free will by now, we are bound to confess that we have not even entirely succeeded in dashing our own, let alone, of course, anyone else's. Free will may be an illusion — if everything was electrically predetermined from the outset, we merely go through the motions and feelings of it — but it is, at any rate, a necessary illusion. We cannot live without it. If we believed ourselves to be entirely and only creatures of circumstance, we might well be inclined to sit down and do nothing, to give up the whole thing as a bad job, so that life would come to a standstill. As as we cannot bring ourselves to believe this, life is evidently determined to go on, through us. In order to struggle on, which means in order to live at all, we are bound to believe that we have at least some measure of free will. And "some measure" may just conceivably not be completely untrue. There is perhaps room for it in this way. The general trend of evolution, as we see it, is upwards, allowing at the same time for what we should call numerous false steps, from the dinosaur downwards, the process being a rough and ready one of trial and error. Julian Huxley's explanation that progress can be accounted for by life's natural tendency always to seek the easy way and go into odd unoccupied corners (avoiding the midst of the melee by developing new forms that can utilize material means of existence not already claimed by others) is a determinist explanation in that this "natural tendency" is given beforehand.

The new developments, the progress upwards, will also be inevitable, since existing conditions are also given. The whole process depends upon the given urge of life to maintain itself at all costs. We have described that urge in terms of radiation which cannot but go on radiating. But the essence of the phenomenon of man is that man is conscious of the process; he is evolution come to consciousness. If, therefore, man consciously puts himself in the generally upward stream of evolution, feels himself part of the stream, he may become at any rate a voluntary participant in it.

Whether voluntary participation is quite the same thing as free will seems to us rather doubtful. It appears to be at least restricted. However, we never expected to arrive at more than "some measure" of free will, and wishing to avoid the mental acrobatics of Bergson in this connection, we feel that we must be content with what little we have, and only hope we have succeeded in arriving at it honestly.

Yes, at this great span of time, we can surely feel that our author did write honestly, and that subject to the limitations of outlook of his age, to various shortcomings and misconceptions which there is no need to detail, this was a surprisingly farsighted view to take. If ever the future cast its shadow before, it certainly did in this case. With most of the contents of the first extract in particular, we have comparatively little quarrel even today, disregarding sundry matters of detail. Time has proved that the writers to whom our author made reference were indeed among the "immortals" of his century, which every study of the period must include. But one prominently relevant writer is absent from our author's references, as readers conversant with ancient thought will have noticed already, for a certain parallelism seems to show here and there. There is an explanation for this, and we shall give it in our author's own words, which he adds to his work by way of appendix. But first we want to complete the main set of his extracts by appending the short section he wrote at a later point in his book, on Emil Durkheim, a profoundly philosophical sociologist of Franco-Jewish origin, dating to the beginning of the twentieth century. He comments on "the social conscience, in effect, which Durkheim postulated" as follows:

What is particularly significant is that Durkheim holds that the socio-moral forces generated by social life itself are comparable to the other forces in the universe. This reminds us of the attitude of the Third Earl of Shaftesbury, who, in his moral philosophy, also viewed moral forces as not being devoid of cosmic implications. We are bound to follow after these thinkers with approval, for the whole purpose of our first chapter, in which we theorised on radiation, was to try to sketch some feasible connection between human ideals and the stuff we and the universe are made of. We sought to do this by extending the concept of brain-electricity, known to exist, to include ultra-micro-wavelengths of quite different nature, not yet known to exist, so tying psychological productions (thoughts) to a material (electrical, radiational) basis. Durkheim almost goes farther than we do ourselves. He claims that society, a product of nature, dominates it, and that all the forces of the universe converge in society, forming thereby a new and higher stage of evolution than existed before. More, he sees society as the highest point of nature, urging itself on, as it were, to surpass itself. This is certainly not unrelated to our own independent formulation of the evolutionary process; but we refrained from waxing quite so lyrical about society, both in the abstract and in the concrete... Durkheim calls the moral the voice of society within us; without it we cannot live, for we are intrinsically organic parts of society — never totally independent individuals.

As against this, it is interesting for a moment to compare some of Durkheim's own words:

Society is the center of a moral life of which the strength and independence have not always been fully recognised. When individual minds are not isolated, but enter into close relation with and work upon each other, from their synthesis arises a new kind of psychic life. It is clearly distinguished by its peculiar intensity from that led by the solitary individual. Sentiments born and developed in the group have a greater energy than purely individual sentiments. A man who experiences such sentiments feels himself dominated by outside forces that lead him and pervade his milieu. Following the collectivity, the individual forgets himself for the common end and his conduct is oriented in terms of a standard outside himself. At the same time, and owing to their theoretical nature, these forces are not easily controlled, canalised and adjusted to closely determined ends. They need to overflow for the sake of overflowing, as in play without any specific objective. . .

And further from his *Sociology and Philosophy:*

Society is of nature and yet dominates it. Not only do all the forces of the universe converge in society, but they also form a new synthesis which surpasses in richness, complexity and power of action all that went to form it. In a word, society is nature arrived at a higher point in its development, concentrating all its energies to surpass itself.

The contrast between the non-reasoned, enthusiastic, mystic and dogmatic writing of the period around the beginning of the century, and the cautious, painstaking efforts of our unidentified author in the middle of it, is obvious in the extreme. The latter writer also had no solid scientific basis for his thesis; he frankly admitted it was but tentative hypothesis. But owing to the discoveries of the decades immediately preceding him, he was able to make a coherent set of suggestions that were generally reasonable and went a long way towards tying up concepts and aspects of man in the universe. Since then, as we know, actual scientific development has done much to justify his proffered scheme of inclusive evolution, which today is broadly acceptable. Durkheim mentions to some extent the same things. He makes no attempt to give them a scientific basis, though. He even alludes to play, as does our own author, but how differently! Intuitive assertions he makes in plenty, and he clearly made careful psychological observations too. In all, his vision was justified no little, and his prominence acknowledged. For all that, no logically inclusive scheme supported his claims. Admittedly, the thought of each of the two writers is on quite a different plane, so the comparison is not really fair. Even so, it may be held to be definitely illuminating in regard to twentieth century scientific thought.

Before we part company from the unknown author, there is obvious need, as has undoubtedly been inferred by the knowledgeable reader from what we stated previously, to set him in relation to that giant intellect of his century, Pierre Teilhard de Chardin, whose great *The Phenomenon of Man* covers infinitely more deeply the total scope of man's position in the universe. Was there any borrowing by our author (to put it mildly)? The great book mentioned was certainly in circulation first.

We are satisfied, for two reasons which buttress each other, that no such borrowing took place. Our author, in his "postword" as he calls it, devotes himself almost entirely to this topic, fully realizing his position in this respect. He states that of course he knew of the book's existence (it naturally became world-famous at once), but that he had not read it before he wrote himself. As a matter of fact, he sent a copy of the material we have quoted to a friend, who immediately responded with the remark that it reminded him of the Teilhard de Chardin work, and followed this up by lending him a copy of the latter (we learn that overseas postal dispatch was involved). Our author writes:

> On reading it at once, I was not less than astounded to find that without much exact parallelism (although even this was not lacking in places) it was evident I had been thinking somewhat on Chardin's lines. Many readers, well acquainted with his book, may well think that I borrowed basically from him; but if they reflect that I based myself, with duly expressed appreciation, on another book altogether (by Köhler); that I concentrated particularly on extra-sensory perception, which Chardin does not specifically bring into account fundamentally; and that, except once or twice at the very end, he does not use the concept of radiation in my purely literal sense of radio-broadcasting at all; I think they will see that insofar as I do seem to echo Chardin in my petty and partial way, it was genuinely a coincidence.

Our author goes on to explain that whereas his basis was short-wave radio, Teilhard de Chardin's was palaeontology. This is what provides us with our second reason for believing it to be unchallengeable that our author wrote independently. The basis of thought is entirely different. This is evident from both the material and its style of presentation throughout. So we are only too pleased to grant our stimulating author his originality, while recognizing, as he also states quite frankly himself in his "postword," that, soon after mid-century, thought was in any case tending towards formulation of such concepts in the scientific world. At all events, priority not only in time but altogether in sheer quality and grandeur of thought, remains with the great classic writer in question. Contemporary humanity was indebted to Teilhard de Chardin for an entirely unique enlargement of outlook, almost impossible to assess adequately. Nevertheless, our minor and unknown author made a contribution which has surely been revealing, worthwhile, and of convenient dimensions for readers of this study.

All the available evidence, though, leaves us in no doubt whatever that, for the most part, he was by no means taken seriously in his time. The whole tone of the scientific outlook then was restricted and conservative in the extreme. As opposed to the inclusive view, in which all natural phenomena, of whatever type, are interrelated (an approach taken for granted in our own days) everything seems to have been cut up into separate little sections, which scarcely anyone ever thought of combining in an intergrated manner. Not only was society atomized; inevitably, science was, too. The division between the social and the natural sciences was so extreme that it gave rise even then, among more intelligent people, to the famous complaint of "The Two Cultures." The social scientist could not communicate with the natural scientist, for even if he used the same words (which would have been unusual, as different vocabularies prevailed to a quite exaggerated extent), he used them in a different sense, based on different concepts. If, by way of rare chance, some attempt was made to produce an integrated statement concerning the human scene, it was, in fact, not integrated at all; that is to say, it was not tied up with any natural-science backing. It took the shape of a Durkheim-like statement, for instance, without the slightest material explanation. No doubt this was fundamentally due to the lamentable dualism, that unfortunate division between mind and matter, which had plagued mankind from very ancient times into ancient ones; a childish misconception indeed, all too typical of the childhood of the race. The social sciences were put, consciously or unconsciously, into the department of mind (in spite of factual statistics necessarily being included in their basis; economics was an interesting half-way house, but it was not generally realized what a very mental science it basically was), and the natural ones in the department of matter, and there you were. (Mathematics was the interesting half-way house in the latter department. We have of course long since learned that it is fundamentally an expression of the electrical structure of our brains, but that was only slightly recognized a millenium ago.)

So the importance of the Teilhard de Chardin breakthrough, and even of writing such as that of the unknown author, can readily be appreciated nowadays. But, in addition to the great gulf separating the social and natural sciences, there was grave and even fatal division between the sciences on the same side of the gulf, this applying to both sides of it. Coordination of research was extremely difficult to achieve. In a contemporary plea for organizing institutes to investigate and test methods of social change directed to the conscious improvement of society, a certain very perceptive Professor Fairweather in the North American region expressed matters thus:

> But the academic institution has also established another norm which has prevented concentration upon significant social problems. This has been the emphasis that each discipline is a separate subject matter. The humanities, social sciences and physical sciences are perceived as discrete entities with little or no overlap. Therefore, it is most difficult for students in separate disciplines to obtain perceptions integrating these discrete subject matters into a meaningful whole. . .
>
> The academic institution, therefore, by defining its research as "pure" and thus, without regard to social need, by treating its subject matter as separate rather than integrated and by establishing status on the basis of number of publications, has successfully isolated itself from the community. It has become a relatively independent organization with its own social system which functions in a detached manner from society at large. Since students are shaped by institutional norms, few experimental methods aimed at systematically introducing and studying social innovations to solve critical social problems have been developed.
>
> But the social value of these three traditions — social scientists' naive attempts to emulate the physical scientists, the lack of a mechanism for rational social change, and the academic institutions' isolation from industrial, political and other social institutions — is now being seriously questioned by social scientists and community leaders alike. . .

We cannot go into detail concerning all the points this writer mentions in this short but meaningful extract. Especially significant (and ridiculous from our point of view) is his stress on the isolation of the academic institution from society as a whole. This basic fault alone explains much of the unsatisfactoriness of twentieth century civilization. It is clear, though, that a fine grasp of the essential position had been attained in this instance. Towards the end of the century, it is true that a great deal of questioning and no little improvement set in; the first beginnings of the transition to the modern period. However, research by the relevant historians shows that this writer's statement was among the earliest in this vital direction. As it was, academic study seemed to result in leaving questions unanswered. Any attempt to provide answers apparently invalidated it at once!

This absurd attitude was at least partly due to sheer lack of basic knowledge. Such basic knowledge was indeed hinted at in the exceptional writings we have quoted, but it was not yet factually established or coordinated. So, in effect, in spite of their appreciably advanced technology (within its limits) the ancients of the twentieth century were not so enormously better off than those of the tenth (although they certainly thought they were! – and in some specific fields were undoubtedly justified in so thinking), or even than the very ancient peoples. We speak, of course, in absolutely general, overall terms. An adequate, whole, scientific grasp was undeniably still lacking in those times.

The thoughtful men of that period used to write at their best like this, for example:

> ... It is man's duty and destiny to carry on the process of evolution by utilising all his powers for the betterment of himself, for the improvement of his spiritual and physical welfare, for the increase of his knowledge and of the power with which this knowledge can endow him, for the reshaping of the world into a fitter place for human beings to live in, for the attainment of more exalted and more fundamentally satisfying experience – in a word, for what we mean by Progress in the widest sense. The problems of science, art, philosophy are inexhaustible; the Universe presents endless possibilities for the exercise of human daring, skill and ingenuity. It is a battle that can and must be fought on many fronts: by the sociologist who endeavours to understand the laws of social development, by the artist who satisfies our longing for aesthetic experience (that unique craving of the human mind), etc. The stage is set for the epic struggle of Man versus the Universe.

That comes from a contemporary book by Flugel, *Man, Morals and Society,* and is undeniably admirable. It sets forth the challenge boldly, clearly and inspiringly. But it was not the author's fault that there was nothing behind it by way of really comprehensive scientific knowledge and outlook to enable a concrete broad and deep start to be made. Decades more of piecemeal blundering, on the basis of misconceptions, however well intended, or on that of no conceptions at all, were yet to follow before, at last, the various uncoordinated experiments began to become integrated and subsequent centuries were able to forge strongly ahead.

Perhaps we should not be too hard on the unfortunate folk whose mental outlook we are trying to reconstruct in imagination. After all, we can but reiterate that scientific progress had not really gotten far in that early period. Those who lived in it indeed dwelt in ignorance. Although so much is so obvious to us today, because we are heirs to a comparatively advanced cultural tradition, they were constantly baffled by matters we have no difficulty in explaining. All we can perhaps blame them for is their usually not even trying to guess in the direction of an explanation. That mental inertia, as it seems to us, was no doubt the product of their deadening and frustrating social circumstances, but only a highly specialized study can work out details of all the interaction involved.

For further exemplification, let us turn back to a contemporary book from which we have already quoted, J. B. Priestley's *Rain upon Godshill:*

> ... profound emotions, which enrich our lives, are tests of and clues to our essential nature, to the innermost self, and certainly they do not belong to the small rational world, the little surface of life they map for us in the text-books. Nor do they merely color the interior of people's lives. They can shape and change the whole outward mode of living. One young man walks into a museum gallery of Egyptian antiquities and afterwards arranges his whole existence so that he can meditate on ancient Egypt. A woman on a long journey comes to a desert and is so deeply stirred that ever afterwards her heart aches to return to it. A man will toil day and night for years so that at last he can retire to a distant island that he knew for one morning. A girl will marry a man because he is the only one within reach who has a certain kind of speaking voice. This call to and response from the essential nature, the innermost self, we call romance, and it is as common as blackberries and yet a mystery.

And again, from the same source:

The difference between us was not in ability, but in the fact that while they at heart did not really much care about authorship but merely toyed with the fascinating idea of it, I cared like blazes. And I suspect that in any form of art, it is this caring like blazes, while you are still young, that counts. Because you care and the dream never fades, other things, looking like those gifts of the gods, are added unto you. The very passion of the heart draws power. In some mysterious fashion, I suspect, you orient your being so that such gifts as observation, invention and imagination are pulled your way. . . . A mere desire for rewards, no matter how constant and burning that desire may be, will not do the trick. You have to be fascinated from the first by the art itself, engrossed and spellbound, and not simply dazzled by the deceptively superior life of its successful practitioners. In this matter you have, in short, to be pure in heart before you can be blessed.

On the face of it, it might seem that these last two extracts belong rather to a dissertation on art than to one on science. Not a bit of it! The essential point is that in the first extract the word "mystery" appears, and in the second the word "mysterious." But to us today there is no mystery and nothing mysterious in any of the phenomena described. We know perfectly well that what Mr. Priestley was writing about was the way in which human experiences affect brain currents on various wavelengths. When the experience is very intense, in terms of resultant brain voltage, the basic inner currents, the essence of that particular personality-complex, are influenced, and the subsequent pattern of life-action is shaped accordingly. Twentieth century people called this romance. We ourselves know it a millenium afterwards as inner electric field reaction. And in the second passage cited here, we should describe the matter in terms of inner beaming of will-current, after such a reaction (which would have been termed then "firing of the imagination," or some such charmingly poetical phrase), resulting in marked concentration and intensification of a predominant section of the brain field, with very definite consequences in the action realm following.

As everyone knows, the mere fact that we can explain feelings scientifically nowadays does not make the slightest difference to the experiencing, intensity, delight or its opposite, of those feelings. All the human side of the affair remains exactly as it always was. We have not taken anything away. We have merely added. And we do not normally think of the addition while we are doing the experiencing. So nothing has changed really. Our art in all fields today is at least as good as it was then; that is to say, it is considerably better than in the case of the commonly degenerate examples of twentieth century art which have survived, obviously, but it is still a matter of dispute whether our peak points exceed theirs or those of other periods in the past. There is still room for more scientific investigation on the basis of the brain frequencies involved in the greatest art of all times. In that most of the arts usually flowered simultaneously in civilizations of the past, and probably still do (it is no simple matter to appraise one's own time accurately, hence the doubt), it is likely that radiationary interaction between artistic personalities is a factor to be considered too. The research is a delicate matter in the extreme and is nowhere near completion yet. The whole business of ebbs and flows in art, as in other human activities, has not yet yielded up its secrets to our investigators; nor can we yet say whether there is a kind of upper limit, which man has been able to reach now and again ever since he attained a certain stage of development, or whether there is, in fact, a very gradual but definite improvement in artistic standards, as in others, from peak to peak, ever onwards and upwards, as would seem to us both logical and pleasant.

In any event, we may well spare a little sympathy for the artists, the thinkers and feelers, of our and other bygone centuries. Those who perceived more deeply than their contemporaries were the forerunners, the human beings a step ahead in evolution in their sensitivity, pointing the way to the more highly developed men of the future. The contrast with the general run must always have been painful for them. Some time ago, a rather mutilated diary of the period under consideration turned up in excavations. It belonged to someone called Wendy, and among the entries still readable in it are one or two very relevant for us at the moment. One such entry is an almost wistful complaint: "Littleness of mind is so universal; there are so few to communicate something." (This may have been intended to read, "there are so few to communicate with." The last word is no longer clear.) And another entry: "The most important things to us are other people." All of which rings so true.

In this context, it is appropriate to quote briefly from that outstandingly philosophical scientist, Julian Huxley, previously mentioned by that unknown author of ours. When dealing with

"Religion and Science" in *Essays of a Biologist,* he wrote:

> A power of personalities is their power of interpenetration.
> The purely material cannot do this. It is another of the great
> differences between the psychozoic and all previous stages of
> evolution, between man and all else that we know in the universe,
> that the discrete units reached at this level of organisation, the
> individual human beings, can achieve interpenetration by means
> of their minds. When you expound a new idea to me, and I grasp
> it, our minds have obviously interpenetrated. This is a simple
> case; but there may be an intimate union of mind with mind
> which is the basis of the highest spiritual achievement and the
> greatest happiness. If mind and matter are two properties of the
> same world-substance, then the rise of mind to dominance has
> enabled this basic substance to escape from some of the
> imprisoning limitations which confined it at lower levels of its
> development; do we not all know that despair at being boxed up,
> that craving for communion? Using our previous line of argu-
> ment, we see that the interpenetration of personalities is right,
> implies a further step in progress, must be part of the basis on
> which future advance in evolution is to build.

It is, of course, interesting to note, as our readers will have done
immediately, a certain parallelling of the thought of our unknown
author once more. But it is clear from the absence of any expressed
radiation theory or any assumed electrification of the "world-
substance" in which mind and matter are indeed brought together, that
this is another coincidental example of the developing thought of the
time. We are prepared to vouch for the independence of our author,
because no really substantial parallels to his exposition have ever been
found. Naturally, we cannot know (and he almost certainly did not
know exactly himself) all the source influences which brought him to
think as he did in the end: somewhat differently from others, but
inevitably not entirely apart. He may indeed have been unconsciously
influenced by Huxley, among others, to some extent.

Be that as it may, what we are looking at just now is the in-
capability of twentieth century people to explain such things as
communion, altruism, and so on. Huxley, for example, suggests no
explanation of the former. He merely states it as a fact, scarcely
separates it entirely from the very different intellectual inter-

understanding (a relation does exist, but it is very complex), and accepts it enthusiastically. Once more, inclusively scientific, integrated coordination of phenomena is absent. It was not even guessed that altruism must be an inherent tendency of interflow of personality radiations, as part of the universal electric energy flow, although Huxley did give human communion a built-in place in evolution, which was an implication in the right direction. Of course, the maintenance of the individual's life current is also utterly basic, and contradictory. Hence the difficulties of living in society! Negotiation between people is a matter of integrating their radiations through the medium of intellectual exchange; no simple matter, owing to the complex brain electric field mechanism involved, and very often impossible because of the opposing strength of the basic non-intellectual personality currents concerned. The frequencies must intervibrate sufficiently for some degree of general underlying sympathy to be attained. A thousand years ago, however, sympathy was not even recognised as a scientific fact at all. Nor for that matter was love, surely the clearest example of intervibrating personality radiations. And, naturally, not its opposite, hate, either.

How chemical everything was! The ancients were so immersed in their material, physical outlook that although they already had some grasp of electrical reality, and even very occasionally got as far as making good guesses at the underlying truth, everything was generally interpreted superficially. They could not help realizing the basic importance of water to life. But they never connected its electrical constitution with fundamental life-current, so missing the essence of the matter entirely. In those days, medicine was applied biochemistry, although doctors tried to use electrical radiationary means to assist its cures by blind psychological approaches. When successful, it was indeed a case of "more by luck than by good management." They knew from experience that meaningless injections or pills (plain water or other innocuous substances) could, on occasion, do much to induce cures, but they never realized, as far as we can tell, that they were inducing brain currents which correspondingly acted upon the body. In the absence of appropriate apparatus, it is true they could not have done anything definite about it even if they had known all; but it does seem to us a pity they worked so very much in the dark. That unbased psychology of theirs, suspended in mid-air, as we like to say, was actually a disaster in that it held up real brain-research progress. They thought they already knew much; but they had barely begun to know at all, really. In present times we naturally go in the first place to the electrical basis underlying the chemical, and, for the most part, with material assistance where required, all medical treatment today is simply electrical adjustment.

There is so much that they might have realized even then, if they had worked things out for themselves afresh, without being hidebound by the old, elementary, chemical concepts. We find none of their books commenting that the same foods eaten by different animals help their growth differently because of different electrical foundations to their bodies causing characteristic growth in each case. There is no such statement as that different species cannot interbreed because of basic differences in electrical frequency ranges producing corresponding chemical differences. The structure of living creatures was, in fact, never linked then to their electrical, radiational fields. They were not in a position to know that the scales of some fish are produced by a persistence of the XB range of frequencies, and so with other details of other creature's bodies. Apparently they never bothered to regret that the human body is normally probably too weak to support giant intellects, when it is considered that an infection, defect or accident can so easily wipe out a mind of perhaps supreme importance. It is doubtful if they ever realized that our complex bodies exist simply for the purpose of serving our heads, where the mind-apparatus is placed. Their doctors and other health-assistants seemed to view bodies as equally important in all their parts, but this is not absolutely true; it is true only for the sake of successful general operation, on behalf of the head. If a human brain could manage with a different, and above all simpler, body-basis, how much better it would be! The human body is too complicated a machine. We have to simplify it. And that is the line of future medical research in the sphere of practical improvement today.

Not that that is our only or even chief activity towards progress in the medical field these days. We know, for instance, that old age is due to an electrical running-down, for chemical cell-renewal continues; there is no purely chemical reason why it should not continue indefinitely. Appropriate electrical treatment can surely lead to immensely longer life; even to immortality, if we can catch the right frequencies (which we may never be able to do, since special complications come into play here). Meanwhile, we can preserve people indefinitely for interstellar flights by putting them in a suitable electrical field, although they have to remain in a state of unconsciousness all that time. Ultimately, we can even hope to reduce people to pure radiation, transmit them anywhere at the speed of light, and duly reassemble them chemically and instantaneously on arrival (which would sometimes be a convenient means of intra-terrestial transport as well) but here again the difficulties are so far well beyond our powers, or even any definitely foreseeable powers, for that matter.

More immediately practical is the possibility of programming people, much as the ancients programmed their computers. But we shall then be placed in the awkward position of having to decide on the various forms of human perfection, a very disputable and relative affair still today. At the moment, we are still held up by difficulties arising out of that same indeterminacy principle known to the ancients, which seems to be preventing us from handling the fundamental personality currents. Some annoyed modern writers have gone so far as to attribute built-in cunning to creation, as though the universe was determined to outwit us! Anyway, the whole matter of tuning people to required frequency complexes is coming up at next year's World Discussion, and is clearly of vital importance.

All these activities and considerations were quite impossible for our twentieth century predecessors. They were indeed familiar with chemical compounds. But it had never occurred to them that there were also electrical compounds of a vast range of frequency types and combinations, and that these were much more fundamental still. Obviously, there can be no chemical compound without the appropriate stable electrical compound, or composite field, behind it. They had a certain amount of electrical technique, but their fatal failing to link up all natural phenomena together into a connected system ensured that when dealing with electricity, they stayed in that area, and when dealing with other things, they carefully refrained from introducing the universal electricity or general energy of the universe into it, although it underlay everything. It is no wonder to us that they did not get far in many fields at all. They actually used the word "shock" for any sudden hold-up of physical processes without apparently sufficient physical cause, as in the case of bomb-shocked people in war, but never realized, it seems, that this was just as much a case of electrical shock to the body's currents, brought about by internal short-circuiting in the brain and consequently damaging excess-voltage, as an electric shock given by an external current which they did recognize. It is difficult for us nowadays to think ourselves back into a more elementary mental state, but if we reflect, we can perhaps understand that, in such an earlier stage, to remain in the field of electricity was intellectually simple enough; but when electricity literally took on flesh, as it were, and became the partly chemical, material, human body, it was too difficult for them to conceive, all that time ago. Electrical-energy beingness is inherent in the structure of the universe; but it was beyond them to grasp as much.

We could go on and on, trying to convey the scientific position in the twentieth century by contrasting it with that in the thirtieth. The ancients of those days worried and wrote a great deal about happiness, for which they searched no less than we, and considerably less successfully. They experimented hedonistically; they even came to correct conclusions that happiness is obtained by self-immersion in deep interests, the affairs of other people, self-forgetfulness in general, including that of intense artistic experience, whether creative or appreciative. As usual, explanation was not forthcoming. As far as we have been able to ascertain, no one ever suggested that happiness was just a matter of human electric currents flowing the right way at the right strength on the right wavelength for the structure-field of the individual concerned. Conscious self-effort to find happiness simply holds up these currents, turns them inwards and involves any amount of short-circuiting which, at the worst, is typical of actual neuroses. But neuroses of unending variety were so typical of that century in particular that we are appalled by the statistics our researchers dig up. What we want to do today is to find ways of accentuating human sensitivity mentally and emotionally, while enormously reducing it physically, so as to cut out pain except in very reduced degree as nature's warning of something wrong, needing attention. This again is a very difficult and delicate matter, totally inconceivable a millenium back, of course; but we hope to develop the tools in the near future. We shall be very greatly helped by the electro-physics lessons now being received by our radio-telescopes from the second planet of the star RL7 at 700 light-years' distance, so kindly arranged for us by our thoughtful predecessors of the twenty-second century.

Lack of space prevents us from adding many further notes to our treatment of this subject. We may remind our readers that a thousand years ago not even control of the weather had been achieved. It was indeed mentioned, but atomic energy had not been developed sufficiently to be useful for shifting masses of air around in millions of tons as required. So the twentieth century folk had to put up with all kinds of inclement weather, being quite unable to do anything about it. They used to read and hear so-called forecasts of what weather was coming their way, but so poor were the techniques available that not even these were very accurate and frequently were wildly erroneous. This, however, was an outstandingly bad example of their practical technology in general. By and large, their mechanical prowess was already notable and successful in making much of the world more amenable to human needs. This alone was obviously not nearly enough: from the social point of view, science could not be applied where it was wanted, for outworn individualistic organization and customs interfered (the Eastern Bloc did do better in this respect by reason of its much more collectivized social organization, but also came up against failings in other fields); and from the scientific standpoint itself, as we have seen, everything was fragmented, incomplete, and unnecessarily far from a working synthesis.

Synthesis. That is the key word for our conclusion here. The lack of a reasoned synthesis, not only of the various sections of scientific endeavor itself, but of science together with cosmology, art, and philosophy, was what spoiled the scientific picture of the twentieth century and made the scientific position then so unsatisfactory. The right things were not infrequently done, either for the wrong reasons or without any scientific basis or justification whatever. We may explain ourselves by referring to a statement on record made by an American orchestral conductor called Stokowski in a British broadcast interview at the end of the year 1965. He made the then astonishing remark that music is the vibration of air waves which can influence the mind towards ethical good through body and brain. He can have had no possible solid scientific foundation for saying anything of the sort. In fact, almost no one could have had at that time. But, as the quotations and other comments in our above discussion show, reasons can be worked out in support of the extraordinary statement concerned, as it then was, and if a little mixed, incomplete and partly dubious, we do not see anything very unusual about it today, any more than the most daring thinkers, few as they were, might have done then. The population as a whole, though, would necessarily have to regard the statement as fantastic and not to be taken seriously. We cannot tell, but we suspect that Mr. Stokowski was speaking vaguely, metaphorically, or virtually poetically, or that he held what amounted to a mystic belief in this connection. That he could have worked matters out fully on our lines is inconceivable, because the phrasing is so inexact and even inappropriate altogether, that if he had, by a rare chance, read the decidedly rare literature from which we have quoted, he would have phrased matters somewhat differently even in a brief interview.

Music is indeed one of the most powerful of the arts in its radiational brain influences. Its effect is the same in any surroundings: it has the effect of annihilating space and time, as indeed all art can do at its best, but usually to a much less intense degree, although no few exceptional mental field structures react otherwise. Music is also exceptionally powerful in temporarily banishing tiredness. Any intense interest can do this up to a point, but none better than music, which does suggest a strong direct connection with those brain currents, forming the fundamental flow of consciousness, that are infused with new strength through activation of the aural apparatus on musical frequencies. Modern researchers are still working on this problem. But to connect music directly with ethics is to go further than we have reached even now! However we no longer rule it out as a possibility, as the twentieth century general public undoubtedly would have done.

Disconnected sciences, dissociated from each other and everything else, do not constitute science in our view, for fragmented, isolated, unrelated science is largely meaningless to us. The requisite synthesis was not achieved until appreciably later than the century under review, but its first stirrings did appear precisely then, as our contemporary quotations prove. Science needs to be a science of man, and of man in his universal setting, which is all-inclusive. Twentieth century scientists were evidently too early on the stage of human history to establish this fundamental set-up. Only their successors were able to achieve the synthesis and provide the basis for building the happier world we enjoy today.

# 3 The Literary Position
## A Lyrical Interlude

Outstanding among the centuries of the ancient world, the twentieth has long been famous for plumbing the depths of literary degradation. In view of the socio-moral collapse its civilization suffered, there is nothing surprising in this. The literary field in question has been subjected to close scrutiny by many competent scholars of subsequent centuries, and the current millenary publications include further fine appraisals. These are by no means restricted to the negative side of the subject; although abnormally low in quantity, this significant transition century did have its literary highlights as well. Nor are they even minor ones, in many instances. Here and there fine works of the period have survived the test of time and taken their place in our heritage to prove that the human spirit at its best was still in evidence even then, if somewhat dormant on the whole, pending later reflowering. In music, incidentally, the achievements were decidedly finer still. Besides, this was the century which saw the beginnings of electronic music, realized by very few then to be the music of the future, but obviously the standard form in subsequent times — for not only can all the sounds of ancient instruments be reproduced electronically, but also all other sounds whatever — although, naturally, individual instruments are ever used for personal expression. And of course, the name of that unique twentieth century artist, Walt Disney, is undying on account of the profoundly human artistry of his exquisite fantasy films which are reissued century after century, classics complete with their delightful old-fashioned music, to charm children and adults alike.

But it is the literature of that century with which we are concerned here, and our approach is going to be unusual. We shall attempt to convey what was by presenting what was not — to express the matter in only very slightly exaggerated form. It so happens that (a few years ago) the present writer found an item (once more from the islands of Britain) in the World Literature Museum which had been almost entirely neglected in research. There was good reason for most of this neglect. The quality of the book, judged from almost every standpoint, was beneath all criticism. It was extremely bad, absurdly naive, and even childish writing. But on one score, and one only, it passed with flying colors. It was devoid of decadence. Entirely unsatisfactory as a literary production, it was uncomplicated and optimistic throughout, totally untypical of its period. Except that it is not clear whether it was ever intended to be literature at all, it might have belonged to the previous century, when writing was still healthily vigorous.

The book to which we allude is an incredible mixture of music and politics, of all things. Its sections are headed in accordance with the movements of Beethoven's Fifth Symphony, that grand old classic of the past, and there seems to have been an attempt to fit the tempo and spirit of the sections to the movements of the symphony. This was hardly more successful than in the case of another such rare example known to us from the twentieth century. The author refers to the matter in the course of his writing, being almost oddly self-revealing. Unfortunately, we do not know his name or anything about him, this being another instance of an ancient book with cover and title-page missing. It is clear, though, that it was written during, or soon after, the Second World War: it is full of historical and geographical references. How it ever managed to get published is beyond our comprehension today; it is totally outside the spirit of its time, a century too late for its market. But it is just on that account that we bring it into our twentieth century picture now. The reader has only to imagine the opposite to the extracts we bring from it, and he will have quite a good idea of the actual literature of the twentieth century in general!

The book is called *European Symphony* and it starts as follows:

> The last great chords of Beethoven's Fifth Symphony crashed proudly across the hall. It was the end of a truly fine concert, whatever quibbles the critics might indulge in during the course of their comments in the morning papers about it. And well it need be, thought Peter Midford; it was not every day that a celebration concert like this took place and it was just as well the British Philharmonic Orchestra had risen to the occasion, considering the number of foreign dignitaries present.
>
> Then he remembered — they weren't foreign any more. Not

most of them, at any rate. The French, the Dutch and the others in the brand new United States of Europe were just as much Europeans as he was. It would take a little getting used to, this common citizenship, but it wasn't any more strange than Scots and Englishmen both being Britons for that matter; even the blundering generation of his parents had accepted that as normal, although the very idea of it would have been laughed at a few centuries earlier. But Sabini, the fiery conductor from Milan, had returned to the rostrum and Peter joined wholeheartedly in the renewed applause.

In the middle of it, he thought he felt a soft weight resting on his left foot. Standing as he was, in the fashion of a seasoned Promenader for old times' sake in the splendidly rebuilt and enlarged Queen's Hall, he noticed it at once and smiled openly upon finding it was a small tabby cat. A cat on the floor of Queen's Hall was a new idea at a concert! Promenaders always used to have odd habits of their own, but bringing cats to Queen's Hall was definitely beyond normal practice. Doubtless it belonged to the place, but it was almost unbelievable that it should wander among the audience at a concert instead of keeping in the corridors or cellars or wherever it was supposed to live. It even had an identity disk on a mauve ribbon round its neck.

Peter grabbed the cat hurriedly as it started to move away (frightened a little by a last outburst of clapping at the final reappearance of Sabini) and holding it firmly under his right arm, read the name on the label with something like amazement. 'Pongo Allison, 22 Oakle Road, Princebury,' it said. The cat licked its tail. It certainly appeared that the animal belonged to Winifred Allison, one of the first violins in the orchestra, whom Peter knew very well by sight. But this was rather like jumping to conclusions with insufficient evidence, for while he had heard that Miss Allison came from somewhere in the Hendon district, he did not know she lived in what was actually his own suburb. It was just possible that another Princebury Allison might have brought a cat and lost it, but Peter decided that was very unlikely.

Amid smiles from those standing near, he put the cat on the floor while he collected his belongings at his feet, and, in answer to two girls who asked him what he was going to do with it, said he would take it round the back of the orchestra and try to trace its owner there. Being, like many other concertgoers, not yet very used to the new Queen's Hall, it took him nearly ten minutes to find his way round to the band room, and inquiries hither and thither failed to produce the required violinist. Eventually, Aileen Wayne, the 'cellist, reported that she had gone home in rather a hurry. There was no alternative in Peter's mind to taking the cat home with him and calling at the address on its little label as soon afterwards as was convenient.

Fortunately, Pongo was a well-behaved small animal, and, resting in Peter's arms along with a couple of books, was not at all perturbed by the escalator at Oxford Circus underground station. In the train, it soon went to sleep, and hardly responded to Peter's giving it an encouraging stroke at about every third station along the line. It was only a short walk through the suburban roads of Princebury to Peter's house and introductions between Pongo and his parents took place rapidly and with considerable amusement on Mr. and Mrs. Midford's part.

'We never know what impressions you are likely to bring back from a concert,' said his father, 'but we don't usually look to your bringing the orchestra's pets home with you.'

'I don't definitely know that it is an orchestral pet yet,' Peter carefully reminded them.

'Too late to make sure tonight in any case,' said his mother. 'Supper has been waiting half an hour already — and now I shall have to find some for your new friend. Give him to me and I'll fix him up in the kitchen. It's Sunday tomorrow and there'll be plenty of time to find out all about him then.'

Pongo was not even mentioned over supper; there was so much else to talk about. Mr. and Mrs. Midford had had to attend a dinner at the Architects' Club, of which Mr. Midford was a prominent member. They were very annoyed at having to miss the concert themselves on account of the clashing dates. 'Idiotic to hold the dinner on a night like this,' Mr. Midford grumbled; 'Ought to have postponed it without a doubt. Let's see that program again.'

Peter handed it over for about the third time. It certainly was a remarkable looking program in more ways than one. The display of colorful flags on the cover was unified, as it was meant to be, only by the outsize European one on top; inside, the Act of Europe was printed in full, jubilatory messages greeted the

formation of the new federation and a full list of the innumerable
celebrations in the member states, of which this concert was one
with many counterparts, occupied several pages. It took several
seconds of fiddling the pages to find the details of the concert
itself:

| | |
|---|---|
| Federal Waltz, The Blue Danube | Johann Strauss |
| March, Pomp and Circumstance No. 1 | Elgar |
| Symphonie Fantastique | Berlioz |
| Symphony No. 5 in C minor | Beethoven |

   'I shall never be able to get used to the idea of the *Blue
Danube* as a federal waltz, will you Joan?' queried Mr. Midford
with almost a suspicion of a sneer in his tone.
   'No, I don't suppose I shall, Henry.' Her voice was not quite
convincingly firm, but probably that was only because she was
not sure whether there would be enough lettuce to go round the
next day.

There is plenty more of this elementary material, which we shall
certainly not reproduce, although it continues to add to the picture of
typical British suburban life in those days and is of some historical
interest. At any rate, the cat is duly restored to its owner, the hero and
heroine of the story thus meeting, and nothing worth while to us
appears until, somewhat later, Peter goes to visit some Central
European friends not far away, called Karl and Susi. The author here
makes the opportunity to explain his own odd style of writing, adds
some contemporary literary comment – we hesitate to call it
criticism – and, interestingly to us after the conclusion of the last
chapter, adds a thought about the inspiring effects of great music on
people. This last is a very oblique, generalized suggestion, in no way
directly connected with our scientific approach to the matter.

   'I first had the idea of writing a book which should be a rehash
in words of what a musical work was in notes,' she began.
   Peter sat up with such a jerk that he knocked a spoon onto the
floor.
   'Oh, it isn't at all exciting in practice. I had to drop it soon
after the start; it wouldn't work in any case. I began by sketching
out a simple story with the score of Haydn's Symphony No. 102
alongside: you ought to know that gorgeous example of late
Haydn if you don't already; it's always quite outrageously

neglected by comparison with the *Surprise,* the *Military,* the *London* and the other famous Haydn symphonies. Anyway, I drafted out a plan, having a theme to balance each one of Haydn's, developing each more or less to the extent he developed his setting it all out in sections corresponding to those of his tempo indications. I was worried by the difficulty of dealing with the repeats from the first, and they were what soon convinced me the whole thing was impossible. You can repeat a musical tune with advantage if it is a good one in the first place, but you can't repeat a theme written in words, even with fairly subtle changes to vary it; readers of prose couldn't possibly stand for it. It's different with poetry; but the basic technique of poetry, with its metre considerations and its atmospheric tone-painting, is closer to that of music than that of prose, so it's a relatively simple matter there. Yes, I said 'relatively.' I don't mean it was a simple matter for T. S. Eliot to write his *Four Quartets.* It couldn't have been, in spite of his genius. But at least he could write them. I don't think even Mr. Eliot could have produced a prose version of a Haydn quartet. For that matter, *Four Quartets* isn't even a poetry version of one. The writing is far freer. That's natural enough; a modern composer could probably turn them into a modern quartet successfully enough by making a close trans-literation in terms of pure sound, for modern musical writing is quite free as we know — to our cost; or, at least, to our additional difficulties of understanding it.'

Susi continued: 'At any rate, if Mr. Eliot can write a minuet and trio in prose, with a proper repeat of the minuet at the close,' she said unconsciously in rhyme and rhythm, 'he's welcome to get on with it. I soon found I couldn't. So I tore everything up (except the score of the Hundred and Second, which is in the bookcase over there) and started again. A new idea had occurred to me. I decided to write a book which should combine musical themes with political ones.'

She could not do anything ordinary, to save her life,' Karl interjected by way of aside to Peter. 'Most extraordinary woman all through.'

'Why did you want to do that?' Peter asked her.

'To try to show that music was not divorced from life. You know how it is in the ordinary way. People keep music for special occasions just as they keep religion for Sundays unless they're among the favored few who have learnt better. I think 'all those who feel that we can occasionally do without dinner or breakfast, but that life without a few extra dishes of music or poetry is hardly worth while' — I'm quoting from Van Loon now: I learnt that bit off by heart; it's great, isn't it? — I think all we music lovers have a special duty to the world in difficult days to show that we are not mere dreamers, that all life is one, that music is not to be taken as an escapist drug but is to be used as an inspiration to each one of us individually to go out and do fine things ourselves. There are two ways of listening to music, as you two must have recognised ages ago. You can take it passively or actively. You can let it soak in like opium or chloroform and dismiss it, when you recover, as mere spare time pleasure and nothing more. Or you can share the composer's thought and feeling with him as his composition proceeds, undergo the most wonderful experiences with him in the process and tell yourself afterwards, 'I'm no genius, but if So-and-So could write like that, can I bear to drag through life without the slightest touch of fire myself? Can I afford to? Of course not. It simply isn't good enough. I can't let So-and-So get away with things like that. If he could capture a lump of heaven itself as he did, I can jolly well do a little bit myself too. It won't be anything to compare with his work, but it will be something. I just can't let matters rest after hearing music like that.' And you go away a better woman or man; the concert has done you good as it ought to do.'

Peter twiddled his fingers on the tablecloth in delight. He knew she was so right.

'Well, then; these are times when we've made great strides forward, but we've still got to work hard to hold our gains, make them work and enlarge upon them. I want to make a contribution. My way is to mix politics and music in a book, to show that beauty and efficiency do indeed go hand in hand even if they're not always interdependent.'

Her two listeners nodded encouragingly.

'Through the inspiration which beautiful music affords us, my case is that we have a duty to repay our debt to the greatest of all the arts by playing a leading part in increasing the efficiency of our civilisation, as is so desperately needed if we are to survive at all, thereby, incidentally, directly helping to ensure the survival of music itself along with the rest of our precious artistic heritage.'

'Hear, hear,' said Peter, quite inadequately.

'I told you she was extraordinary, didn't I?' Karl beamed at him. 'The best of it is that she is quite right, too. Moreover, you implied the right thing just then. She ought to be addressing a public meeting. I believe she thought she was!'

Susi did not bother to deny the allegation. 'Neither of you need worry. My book will never be published even if it ever gets finished. No publisher would look at a thing like that. But I still carry on with it, bit by bit. I feel I must, somehow. The material is in me to get down on paper and I can't escape the job.'

'Sounds like real creative impulse to me,' commented Peter.

'Even if it is – and that's terribly doubtful – I haven't the technique to do justice to it,' she said almost sadly, by way of reply.

'What style of writing are you using then?' Peter inquired.

'That's just the point. I haven't any style. I turn out an abominable mixture of pseudo-Dickens, Jane Austen and H. G. Wells, and it all goes wrong on the way.'

The two men burst out laughing simultaneously. 'It can't be as bad as that,' they assured her.

'Can't it?' she replied. 'You only ought to know. Not that I'm going to show you any,' she added quickly. 'You needn't think you're going to get a look in on the job, because you aren't. The latest turn for the worse it has taken is that it seems to be determined to transform itself into a play by the wayside. You see I can't get the political stuff in properly, or even much of the musical stuff for that matter, without using an inordinate quantity of conversation. The whole thing's being positively swamped by conversation at present.'

'If you won't let Peter and I help you with it, I don't see how we can save you,' teased Karl.

'You can't in any event. I'm far beyond salvation.'

'I don't think you need be worried by a large percentage of conversation in your writing.' Peter said in what some of his friends called his bedside manner. 'Plenty of novels are basically conversation if it comes to that.'

'You can't even call my book a novel. It doesn't seem to fit into any proper pattern at all. I haven't thought out what to call it yet. Besides, it keeps on changing as it grows. There seem to be some Virginia Woolf influences creeping into it somehow now, and you know what happens when anyone starts imitating her exquisite writing; they go down the drain altogether.' Susi refused to be comforted on the lines Peter suggested. She was really quite serious now.

'Yes, I do admit there has probably been no finer writing in the English language since Thomas Hardy than Virginia Woolf's,' he agreed. 'She was perhaps first and foremost an essayist. I don't see any harm in your exploring her path; to follow some aspects of it is very different from mere imitation which would, indeed, be deadly.'

'Thank you for those nice kind words,' she smiled. 'Still, I certainly haven't the powers to do justice to the potentialities of the tradition Virginia Woolf created.'

'Tell me,' Peter returned to the attack in friendly fashion from a somewhat different angle, Didn't you give yourself some course of training before you began on the job? – read a lot of modern novels and see how the trick was done and all that?'

'Not a bit of it! I just set sail on my own tack and that was that. When I wander into other people's styles for lack of one of my own, it's quite by mistake. That's all.'

'Well, what's your procedure of writing? How do you begin and how do you carry on?'

'Shall I answer that one?' Susi turned to Karl.

'Why not? You've told me. I think you should reveal your methods to Peter as well: he won't publish them abroad any more than I will.'

She shrugged her shoulders a little. 'As for how I begin, I don't quite know. I just start, with a scene of some sort, and bring my characters into the scene as I go along. The important thing that troubles me is that I set myself a composing speed of twenty words a minute, so as to give myself a reasonable time limit, and, so far at any rate, I can barely reach half that. I have discovered that the difficulty is not one of wondering what to say next; it is almost entirely a difficulty of selection. That is to say, there is so much in one's past experience which one can draw on at every point that one does not know which items are best to draw on at any particular moment. Consequently, one keeps on stopping for sheer embarrassment of riches. In fact, that's what I'm going to do now.'

'Oh, don't do that, it's too interesting,' Peter objected. 'This time I can help you, perhaps, by asking another question or two if you can bear it. Do you think other writers have this same difficulty and do you think there is any parallel between it and that facing musical composers?'

'As to other writers, I can't say; I've never met any. As for parallels with musical composition, yes, I think there are some. You see, when one gets stuck, uncertain of the best way to move next, it is often helpful to look back over what has just been written. One's eye lights again on a word used just now, and that word immediately suggests another which gives the key to a phrase suitable to continue with. In other words, you look back over your melody-pattern and draw the next idea from a figure of notes already used, as it were. I shouldn't be surprised if that was how many composers did their stuff.'

'There's probably something in it.'

'You can draw other musical parallels too. Composition, whether in words or notes, is utterly plastic. You have to make a pleasing, balanced pattern in time from the unregulated mass of raw material with which you're working – all the words in the language, or all the notes under the sun. You have to produce order out of chaos, to reenact, on one's puny scale, the primeval act of creation. Now, until recently, music got over this primary difficulty by remaining semi-crystallised in set forms, such as the sonata form and others which, after a long process of trial and error, had proved to be fundamentally satisfying to Western peoples. To a certain extent, although it's getting freer and freer, it still has to stick to set forms, varied though they may be. Presumably it always must, or in the nature of things, it may degenerate into a mere cacophony of raw sounds.'

'Some people say it has already done this,' interrupted her husband. Susi refused to be diverted.

'Words are never as chaotically free as notes, though. Their meanings, their associations make them form a pattern, however weak, in whatever way they're used. So there never was any definite set of ready-made forms to put words into. Certain forms did develop all the time, of course, but they were usually individual to the writer concerned, unless he was a mere copycat, or a purposeful imitator for some reason. Mind you, I'm talking about prose now, not poetry. Poetry's a different affair altogether. Being so closely associated with music, it had, for similar reasons, to follow in the footsteps of musical form, in its own way, of course, having regard for the fact that words always remain words and can never become notes. It is because they do so remain that they have their limitations, in spite of being used for the most skillful tone-painting on occasion. Music remains the greatest of the arts because it transcends the limitations of words, beginning where they are forced to leave off. Besides, sound is a much more unfettered medium than paint or stone, and that's why, although music has associations with painting and architecture, its effects can be finer than even the best painting or building. That's only a personal view, of course.'

This not uninteresting conversation continues, but our specimen is long enough. We skip to an extract from the second section, "the slow movement." And the tempo is now indeed slow. The main subject is railway trains. This is a most ludicrous topic, mentally compared with modern atomic trains, and undeniably reads outrageously quaintly today. In its own day, it was probably meant to be mildly funny, but we are really in no position to contrast humor across the ages; the imponderables involved, intrinsic and extrinsic, are too much for us. But it is intriguing to let ourselves into the atmosphere of ancient times as far as may be, and this is a good opportunity.

The train was nearly empty. It had three coaches, but one would have been ample. Perhaps it would fill up with people a little farther along. It did nothing of the sort. It set one person down at one station and picked up no one whatever. After completing that business, it chugged along peacefully enough, occasionally almost bursting into a trot, but thinking better of it soon enough to prevent any undue wear being caused to line, locomotive, or coaches.

Eventually, it came to a standstill. It did not stop. That would have been too violent a word to employ. It merely came to a standstill. Peter wondered why. There was certainly no obvious reason. No one could pretend that the line was overcrowded, or anything like that. There was little likeliness of another train being within tens of miles, as far as one could judge. To the utmost limit of visibility, there was a clear line stretching indefinitely in both directions: no sign of a station at all. They could not be far from Famthorne now, for all that.

The train kept absolutely still. It was very quiet. If there was anyone else on board, which was doubtful by now, they were evidently not taking the slightest interest in the position. Peter decided the best way to use the interlude would be to get his case down off the luggage rack and have another look at the priceless letter Peggy Allison had written to him, describing Famthorne Station, so that he could recognise it in a few minutes when the train bothered to reach it. As likely as not, the porters, if any, never troubled to call out the station names on this line, and it seemed so oddly cut off from the world that there was every possibility of the station nameboard being illegible.

This letter had arrived about a week after Peter had been round to Oakle Road, in response to Winifred's telephone, to arrange his weekend trip. He had learnt then that her sister, with her husband, was going down to Famthorne to stay at the family home for a few days. He found the letter easily, put with one or two books, and unfolded it:

'Dear Peter,

'I am in the remarkable position of having nothing to do for an hour or so, because Winnie is doing some special practice with Dad which I have been ordered on no account to interrupt, and George is out somewhere with the car. He is coming back at teatime to take us for a small evening run, so I am in the garden more or less waiting for him and it occurred to me it might be a good idea to let you know a little of what Famthorne Station looks like, so that you know what to expect when you come to it the weekend after next.

'I am not pretending that our local station here is at all notable, but we think a lot of it in a way. This means it is extremely useful as a local landmark; even now, there are not so many trains that they get in the way at the level crossing very often, which is, of course, a nuisance when we want to get the car through. The station itself is placed a few yards back from the road. In consequence, it has a sort of front garden. Nothing much grows in it except extensive and fluctuating heaps of coal and a solitary, curving siding, which comprises our goods yard. There is usually precisely one peculiar old coach of some kind standing on our siding – or occasionally it may be a coal truck – but no one ever seems to know why, nor, apparently, is any attempt made to do anything about it. The rolling stock concerned is evidently left there simply because the railway people do not know what else to

do with it. Then they forget it till next time, and do the same
thing again.

'Famthorne Station, as a structure, has distinctly Gothic
pretensions, but we never take them too seriously nowadays,
because they are little more than a facade. In reality, there is a
minimum of essential and uninspired accommodation backing the
front garden on the down platform, a small shed on the up
platform and a not-so-small bridge over the line connecting the
two sides, with the usual monotonous, faded notices about not
crossing the line except by the said bridge, which no one but the
strangest of strangers ever dreams of bothering about, so don't
you.

'There is a signal-box, by the way, on the end of the down
platform — or just beyond it, to be precise. This box is inhabited
by a real live signalman, who hauls levers over and thereby
waggles the signals in response to little bells that tinkle several
times at intervals long before a train comes. When the signalman
is too tired to be bothered to obey the bells in his box, the train
concerned sidles up and hoots at him very angrily until he
condescends to play with it according to the rules. Personally, I
always enjoy these *divertissements* immensely. They liven up life
considerably, I feel.

'During the war, things were really at their best as far as
Fambridge Station was concerned. It was necessary to use female
labour on the railways, as you know, from soon after the start,
and two ladies were put in to run the station for us, one short and
fat and old, the other tall and thin and young. I had been reading
Valera's famous Spanish novel, *Juanita la Larga,* about that
time — all elementary Spanish students do, and I had chosen
Spanish at school because it was so much easier than French,
which I hated — so I naturally had to christen the two station
ladies Juana and Juanita, after the author's delightfully-portrayed
mother and daughter characters. As it happened, our two were
not even faintly related, but that made no difference; I have
forgotten their real names now, because they soaked only slightly
into village life, these two stalwarts. You might say they formed a
sort of self-contained battalion of their own, they were so tied to
the station as a rule, and when they were not they always used to
travel farther afield. Juanita did more, rather quaintly, if one may
put it like that. On her alternate weekly late shift, she would

persist in locking up the station before the last-but-one down train came in, hop in its guard's van, go and play with her friends on Southburn Station at the end of the line and return on the last train back, to collect tickets from passengers arriving. An intermediate train was put on. Was Juanita deterred? Rather not! She merely postponed her free evening trip till this later train came along and then jumped on it, arriving at Southburn only just in time to rush over to the other platform there for the last one back. I always wanted to know what happened when she was not in time at all and got left stranded at the Southburn end; it must have happened sometimes, because, as you know, train timings have been all over the place during the war. All she could have done, I think, was to walk the couple of hours back (the road zigzags a whole lot on the way, so being much longer than the straight track of the railway), unless she could persuade some wartime goods train or other to stop for her, but they are always few enough in all conscience. Failing that, she would have arrived far too late to look after the final night passengers, unless they had been held up themselves so much that their train never got through till the early hours of the morning!

'Anyway, there never was any hope of buying a ticket at Famthorne Station in the late evenings of the weeks Juanita was on late turn. Everything was as deserted as the grave while she was playing truant at Southburn, until the advent of her sprightly return in due course. It was different when Juana was on duty, it is true. I write "different" not necessarily better. For Juana was addicted to closing up the public quarters of the station and boiling tea in peace on her little stove in the booking office, and it was a moot point whether or not you could persuade her to sell you a ticket late at night, even if there was a stray train or two buzzing about in the vicinity, unless you were a recognised friend of hers. Personally, I was very sorry when Juana and Juanita retired from the public service at our station, but nobody else seemed to worry one way or the other.

'This is a fantastically long letter — it must be one of the longest I have ever written in my life. I can only put it down to the fact that I rather lost myself in my subject; horribly silly of me. I do not think I ought to post it to you at all now. It is much too overgrown. There is no hope of pruning it, though, because I must go and look for George now; he is over an hour late already.

So it is a case of all or none. Perhaps I will let you have it, as it seems a pity to waste it now I have written it, but I shall have to ask you to forgive its deplorable length, for it was not what I meant in the least. Idleness always did breed mischief, I suppose.

'I hope you have a good time while you are here and like it. As I have advertised Famthorne Station to you so fully, I hope you will like the latter, too. It is no mean halt; we are quite proud of it, I assure you.'

The train had started and given up progress as a bad job twice since Peter had begun reading the letter. He had not reached quite so far as the signature when it stopped properly this time, and, before he had time even to realise he was in a station, someone called out very clearly and loudly, "Southburn, Southburn." Horrified, he stuffed the letter into his pocket, grabbed his case and dived out onto the platform. He had evidently succeeded in overshooting Famthorne while engaged in the process of re-reading about it!

We refrain from reproducing any more of this atrociously light-weight material, but would emphasize that it does give a vivid idea of an aspect of daily life in Britain at the time of the Second World War, to say nothing of the very primitive railway arrangements of ancient times. Even in the case of the First World War, let alone other wars of ancient days, we have nothing quite comparable preserved to us. There is additional interest attached to this part of the book under review, since the area of Britain here dealt with has long since changed its character from a coastal to an inland one. The abolition of the North Sea has made all the difference in the world to this district, and readers who may chance to know it now will certainly not be able to recognize it to any appreciable degree in a description of it which appears a little later in the book:

A very strange land it is; drained marshland to a large extent. It sounds dreary, but somehow it does not live up to its nominal character. It tends, on the contrary, to do just the opposite. For instance, although one can see great flat sweeps of land in some directions, there seems to be nowhere where one is entirely out of sight of certain rises in level: low skyline ridges are the very least that persist in turning up, and sometimes much more. So, instead of monotony, there is always variety. It is basically subtle in character; the sky is at least as important as the land. This fact gives the clue to the pervading speciality of the area: spaciousness. There is plenty of room to breathe.

The sea wall is of crucial interest. A great bank of earth, with sharply sloping sides and a footpath on top, it enables one to walk round the edge of this part of the country in a way which, possible also on other sections of this coast, is rarely imitable elsewhere. Elevated a good few feet above the land and the sea alike, one is outrageously isolated in space on the North Sea margin, and unless one pushes forward with vigorous determination, one is likely to become outrageously isolated in time as well. For the going is extremely hard for stretches of many miles, so overgrown is the sea wall path with long, tough grass and weeds, and time schedules are the first things to slip into the sea — or rather into the mud, since the sea wall actually runs slightly inland for some miles, a considerable yardage of mud, tentatively colonised by grasses, separating it from the actual sea-edge.

As we mentioned at the outset, this peculiar book is basically a mixture of music and politics. The political part of the writing is, naturally, much more outworn today even than the rest, but we must certainly give at least one specimen extract, to show how remarkably clumsily the attempt was made to work these two subjects together. The hero and heroine are talking again:

'The butcher's boy comes up here to get acquainted with Sibelius, but the butcher himself wouldn't dream of following suit, although the sessions are just as open to him. He wouldn't come even if he was not too proud to put himself on a level with his boy for once; and we're all level when it comes to the fundamental things of life, anyway. I've seen him in his literally bloody den, and a real, blustering money-maker he is, too. He doesn't understand that all his butchering is, by reason of the inescapable facts of human nature, dedicated to the prosecution of art. No one in full possession of all their senses devotes their life to butchery. It's the artistic things of life butchery's profits buy which count.

'There's a strong tendency in people to turn their business into a kind of perverted art, you know,' Peter suggested. 'The actual practice of his butchery may give him the satisfactions we get in pure art. In fact, that's almost the only way to account for the life-pattern of the major stratum of the middle classes, narrowly devoid of any appreciable actual art as it is: the bank clerk, the novel-reading housewife, the motorist, the football-pool-coupon-filling or other betting-mad shopkeeper, and the rest of them. We can't suppose they've all become so inhuman that they have succeeded in stamping all vestiges of potential art out of their lives altogether.'

'Thanks for the correction, Peter. I'll have to admit that I was exaggerating after all. Let's call it artificial art, this artistic pride and satisfaction in non-artistic things. It deceives its victims utterly and it's so deceptive in effect that I'd failed to notice it. All I know is that it's our job to reveal the truth. We don't want to push anyone anywhere. We just want to ease the blinkers off and let human nature do the rest. When all's said and done, our own natures must be our best guides; they've guided us quite a long way already, or we should still be uttering screeches in the tree tops instead of sonatas in concert halls. There isn't much doubt about which way to go, as long as we can set ourselves free from the old-fashioned snobberies and counter-snobberies which block that way. That means we must choose a socialist path, as we know, or we inevitably get caught up in the vested interests of snobdom, where butchering becomes an end in itself instead of a means to music or any other of the unlimited arts the butcher may prefer. There are plenty of pitfalls in socialism, as we know too, but at least it gives us a chance. Things are looking up a little. The butcher's boy's got as far as Sibelius, which is not bad. He's only half a century behind, and he'll be whistling Schönberg before he's too old to whistle at all if he keeps it up. The old order was all right for our ancestors, but it was too narrow to give their butchers' boys a chance.'

The sentiment is right enough, no doubt, but political understanding was so very elementary in those far-off days that there is nothing really gained by concentrating on that side of the strange book under discussion, so full of misconceptions, inadequacies and sheer bad expression even of what little was indeed known then. We do better to pass that over and return to the writing on music itself, which is at least a nearer approach to actual literature. The two main characters are having another of their conversations, this time talking about someone else.

'Hazel's a first-rate person,' Winifred said. 'I remember one time she came here before, when we had a chamber concert in the music room and we had a particularly good pianist friend of Dad's taking part. He played the Chopin A flat Ballade by way of interlude between the quartet and quintet in which he partici-pated. He turned out a really beautiful evening's work, in fact. In the middle of the Ballade, I half-noticed Hazel had disap-peared — I was concentrating on the performance, because it was quite exceptional, but Hazel was supposed to be sitting next to me and somehow or other she had evidently decided to melt away. I didn't bother at the time, because the playing was so beautiful and, anyway, it wouldn't have seemed right to imitate Hazel's disappearance stunt and leave two empty chairs instead of one by going in search of her. Afterwards, I found out what had happened. She'd found the Ballade just about unbearably beautiful. I don't blame her, either. It was, in a way. She told me later that evening that she couldn't bear to stay in the room with the rest of us and go on listening in company. The Ballade seemed to be addressed to her and her alone, and she crept out through the open garden doors and sidled behind the bushes outside so that she could listen solitarily. She tried to describe to me how she felt; those lovely statements of Chopin, so close to the heart of humanity, coming from the music room, clear and true in the warm summer evening air of the garden, and the miraculous climax when the main theme reaches its full peak of expression in all its augmented force near the end. She spoke with true passion, although she tried hard to keep her voice matter-of-fact. I know just how she felt, because I'd felt very nearly the same myself at the time. You can call it mere emotionalism or whatever you like, if you want to. I don't care a bit. It's that sort of thing which reveals the greatest heights of music. We know that great music is a balance between thought and feeling, and all that. But thought and feeling are so integrated in the most inspired moments of all that they dissolve into something beyond and above their separate selves. These are the great moments of music and one never forgets them. They seem to point to something funda-mental, somehow. I don't know how, and it may be only a delusion. But there it is. You could say that Hazel contacted heaven that night, and I don't blame her.'

'Yes. I really think the ultimate function of music is a personal one; I don't see how it can be shared. To tell the truth, when I go to a concert, I feel the orchestra is playing for me alone; no one else exists, however crowded the hall may be. It was simply that which Hazel experienced when she couldn't bear to stay in the room with the rest of you during the Chopin; hers was an extreme form of the same phenomenon, so extreme that it had to gain expression in actuality. She was making such a strong contact with the personality of Chopin as expressed through his music that she couldn't bear anyone else to be there.'

'I believe you're right,' Winifred broke in. 'You could say that all listening to music was a matter of contacting the composer's personality, the job of the performer being to assist the process in the purity of integrity and not to get in the way. That's how I look on my work, at any rate, and I know the best conductors I've worked under had the same outlook. All the best conductors have, or they wouldn't be best conductors: they'd be virtual criminals, as some of them still are.'

We note here the standard ancient style of romanticized description, without any thought of scientific explanation as we made clear in our previous chapter. There are vague gropings in the right direction in this instance; even as much as this was unusual in ancient literature. There is some more of it as a matter of fact, quite as relevant, and still literature of a sort. Winifred speaks:

'I'd been out in the fields all the afternoon, half reading, half gazing around, loving it all; it must have been an unusually warm day very early in the spring; it happens sometimes, you know, before any of the feel of summer has even begun to develop. It started getting dark very early; it may even have been February as far as I can work it out now – March, anyway – and I had a peaceful weekend off somehow or other. The moon was up by teatime; you know how absurd the moon is as a rule, never there when you want it for a quick walk home from the last train about midnight, and always turning up at some silly time when there's still some daylight about and there's no need for it at all. Well, on this particular early evening, the moon was in full force, just

because there was no need for it to be, and there was a light
breeze, and I walked towards the house from the back; you can,
there's a path up on that side. On the way, I passed the pond we
have at the end of the garden and then I forgave the moon for
poking its nose in when it wasn't particularly wanted, for it was
shining on the rippling water in a charming reflection and I've
never forgotten the effect. There was just the right grey, dusk
mistiness to set it off to perfection. It was a thing which may not
be repeated exactly for years. It made a perfect finish to the
afternoon in the open. Then I went into the house for late tea
and suddenly heard the end of the theme of the Brahms-Haydn
Variations being played with thrilling richness through the
loudspeakers of the music room. I came up to the door and
couldn't go any further. There was something about this
performance which stopped me just there. I stood and listened,
right to the end. I couldn't do anything else. It was far and away
the finest performance I have ever heard of this great work. At
the end, I heard the announcement: it was a radio concert from
Schweizerischer Landessender Beromünster of all places (a lovely
name, isn't it?). Dad had picked it up on the small radiogram in
his study by chance, had recognised its quality at once, switched
it through to the amplifier in the music room, so as to get the full
benefit of the loudspeakers there, and was listening in a corner,
where I hadn't noticed him at all. It was only at the end that I
saw him and went across to his side. – Wasn't it remarkable? – he
said, and I didn't need to reply. We understood each other
perfectly. It was some Swiss conductor, quite unknown to us
before or since, who was responsible for the performance. For
me, I suppose, the effect was even more striking than for Dad,
and certainly he knew how to appreciate its fine points all right.
You see, I was in a specially receptive mood, dictated by my
previous experiences out of doors that afternoon. That was the
finest example I ever underwent of knowing the ecstasy of
sensing in succession the twin loveliness of the countryside and of
music: and there's a subtle interaction you can draw between the
appreciation of natural perfection appealing to our artistic
instincts and that of manmade art inspired, perhaps, by some
related concept. To be not subtle at all, I can tell you I have often
felt the need for the British Philharmonic to come  *en bloc*  to
play Mozart's *Jupiter* Symphony on the flowing hills of the

chalk to the south of Cambridge; although Mozart was remote from them, by a kind of impossible coincidence come true he hit off the very feeling of those superb flat curves in the andante, as it seems to me. Forgive the deliberately contradictory phrasing. It's funny how some music brings certain scenes into one's mind. I'm not referring to program music. That's easy, of course. But perhaps you've also found that something in a work you're listening to brings to mind a picturisation of a stretch of country or even town you know well. I don't know why it is. It may be that the rhythm or harmony pattern of the music links up subconsciously with the intrinsic rhythm of the mental landscape or its own harmony-feeling for one. It works just as much the other way. You know how common it is to think of tunes during the day for apparently no reason at all. It's occurred to me that that may be because, quite unknown to us consciously, the shape of some building, the rhythm of some footfall, may react on our mental stock of melodies and conjure up a correspondingly shaped or rhythmed one from the stock.'

Another distinctly literary piece from our book takes the form of a second letter from Winifred's sister, Peggy. Mention of trains again (the author must have been very keen on them), but this time the writing is definitely serious. There is even more geographical interest in it, in a way, for us still today, for the chalk hills mentioned remain as they were, by no means having appreciably worn down in a mere thousand years. It is true that they are no longer by the sea as when Britain was still an island, as what they used to call "the English Channel" was, of course, filled in at the time the ancient North Sea was, but that is the only difference. The town of Brighton, then on the coast, was excavated afresh a couple of centuries ago, but yielded nothing of interest for our museums.

'Once past the small southern suburbs, it was good to see open farming country again after the cramped dullness of London. The Wealden land was ordinary, but very pleasant. Probably it contained many gentle wonders, but one could not see very far from the line.

'Halfway along, or a little more. And then something extra. Way out ahead, a glimpse of a long, low line on the horizon behind the trees; a line not very long, nor very low, and certainly

not very straight, as I could see after it had swung into view once
or twice more. But already it had an unreasonable importance in
the scene. It was different, utterly different.

'The chalk! The ride suddenly took on a new and vital
importance altogether. The train was hurtling south into the
chalk and as it did so, the smooth, unique outlines of the Downs
became themselves. They drew nearer and nearer as the train
flashed down coastwards to meet them, the components of 'that
majestic range of mountains,' as I remembered Gilbert White
calling them in his 'Selborne.' How right he was! After a little,
one could separate the 'mountains' as they turned from grey to
green, becoming ever clearer as the train raced on nonstop. The
low evening sun cast a wonderful golden glow over them in parts,
illuminating them with unpaintable beauty. Far, far to the west
they stretched: Chanctonbury with its noble crown of trees,
'monarch of the range,' they call it. On the other side too, away
eastwards, a shorter line of Downs there and straighter, as seen
from the Brighton rail route.

'At last one came really close, and the chalk could be
appreciated in something like its full glory. One could open one's
hand and mentally let one's fingers rest in those soft, shapely,
folded combes, the little dry valleys so typical of the range. One
could virtually stroke the subtly soft whaleback slopes. That was
it: they were almost alive, like gigantic lions resting ponderously
and massively in front of the sea, between the waters and the
Weald, yet with the full grace and graciousness of those giant cats
themselves.

'The secret of the South Downs is quite magic. There is no
reason on earth why their superb slopes and curves, lines and
steeps, should yield an impression of such inspiring power, but
perhaps there are reasons not on earth for the amazing phenomenon. I wished I had read more about their geology; something to
do with the uplifted bed of an ancient chalk sea rearing itself in
waves across southern Britain, the crests of the chalk waves
wearing off and leaving only the present shrunken remains,
eventually to disappear altogether as they have in the lower
Wealden district between the North and South Down ranges. The
northern range is not worth so very much, owing to its concealing
tree cover for the most part—but the southern! How lucky to be
living now and not in the distant past before the chalk had been

furrowed by rain water so beautifully into its present shapes, nor in the distant future when other millions of years of wearing down will have left nothing at all! But this was not geology; it was more like a natural solidification in chalk of the spirit of Art itself. For no reason whatever, but then there never is any particular reason about the best things in life, or, at any rate, none that we have been able to discover yet.

'Bushes, chalk pits, chasing cloud shadows; they were all there before the train dived through the range to tunnel to the coast, although it was only a few moments before it did. There must be many grand train rides in the world — across the Alps, over the Andes, through the Rockies — but these are comparatively outrageous. Perhaps no train ride is more exciting than the simple one down the Brighton line if you know how to look at it and feel what you see. The Downs are sensible, friendly, helpful hills, just about the last word in mountains, free from obscuring trees, beautiful, completely satisfying.

'Afterwards, we slowed down into Brighton. Ridiculous! Brighton wasn't true. It couldn't be after sights like those seen just before. It was nothing more than a bad joke; not real at all. Best to flee back a few miles and to walk out onto the chalk. Grey clouds purr in from the west on a low breeze; those South Downs almost sigh drowsily as they stiffen a little and, reclining more majestically than ever in the silent solitudes of their intimate remoteness, sleep beside the sea in the stillness of the southern night.

'They are the most peaceful hills on earth, surely, these hills of the chalk, here in its finest form. Sparkling in the sun, resting lazily in the grey light of wind and rain, hiding shyly behind a mist curtain; magnificent by day, fearfully mysterious in the impossible noncoloring of night, they alternate between peaceful power and powerful peace.'

These references to the British chalk hills show that the author was well acquainted and impressed with them. They have scanty counterparts elsewhere, and still today can make good pegs to hang literature upon.

Near the end of the book, there is a faintly amusing passage, utterly full of ancient-world atmosphere. It brings us back up against those primitive times when cows were still to be found on farms and not in zoos; when they were yet being utilized as little mobile milk factories and not being preserved as living museum items from the past. The hero and heroine are now visiting friends in those very chalk South Downs.

The Roberts children ran out to meet them as they approached the gate of Swandene Farm. They were named Adagio and Rondo. Their father had originally hoped to have a complete string quartet of children, but as the existing members were already seven and nine years old, this now seemed unlikely. Adagio was already developing promisingly on the violin and Rondo seemed fairly well inclined to tackle viola or cello in due course, so, with their mother at the keyboard, a piano trio at least would presumably be in stock at the farm later on. Their father himself, in spite of his devotion to music, was a rather dubious asset as a second pianist. Farming complications clashed deplorably with practice, as he freely admitted, and one could hardly hope for much.

He was not available at teatime that day, but there seemed to be a fully crowded table in the kitchen when the two children joined their mother, and Peter and Winifred took their places. That was why Peter's chair, against the door, seemed to leave him insufficient room to sit down squarely. Although it was unusually small for a farm kitchen, probably because part of it had been turned into something else a few centuries back (the farmhouse was a rather quaint little flint building), it was not as small as all that. Barbara pointed out that the door was not quite shut, so she reached across and put it to. After a few moments, though, Peter again seemed to be having trouble with the door and Barbara decided they would all have to get up and draw the table farther into the center of the room.

The first part of this process consisted in removing a few sacks of poultry food and suchlike oddments from where someone had inappropriately dumped them, so that they could have more room. They had nearly finished shifting them, mostly by dragging them across the floor (which was of old brick) causing a good deal of scraping, when something made Winifred turn round.

'Good heavens!' she exclaimed, 'Your zoo's escaped!'

'My what?' Barbara asked quickly, turning round and smudging her yellow dress with a streak of some red substance from one of the sacks. Then she nearly fell backwards.

'Mary! Have you gone mad? For goodness' sake go back!' Jumping forward, she tripped over a small heap of logs the children were engrossed in moving in the wrong direction, and Peter only just managed to catch her. They thus all managed to face the door more or less simultaneously, and the children gave a shriek of laughter on seeing what the trouble was. The others could not help joining in, including Barbara herself, who moved forward more cautiously, this time in the role of leader of a small army assembled to turn back an invader, now that she could size up the position.

Half their tea had already disappeared, for, with ludicrously delicate appreciation, Mary, a beautifully modelled Guernsey cow, was sweeping up sandwiches with her tongue in the most efficient manner imaginable. Betraying all the typical immovability of her race, Mary demanded the most pushful efforts of all five to turn her from her tea. In fact, it was a particularly awkward manoeuvre because of limited space, and a good deal of discretion had to moderate the pushfulness in the sense that energy had to be applied sideways at the most inconvenient angles, which reduced its effectiveness considerably. It took nearly ten minutes to edge Mary off and get her back to her own quarters, a task Adagio, through long familiarity with that last area of operations, accomplished single-handed.

Reassembled in a more central position in the room — quite unnecessarily, as Peter pointed out, since there was now no undue pressure upon the door by marauding livestock — and supplied with replenishments of tomato and other sandwiches, tea was at last able to proceed in comfort.

'She didn't break a single cup with her long tongue,' was Rondo's comment. Within a minute everyone was praising the cow's table manners to such an extent that one would have thought she had been specially invited to tea that afternoon. No one had ever heard of such an enterprise on the part of a Guernsey, or for that matter any other make of cow, so commentary subsided after they had agreed it would be the job of Farmer Roberts himself to give an explanation when he came in and received a report on the incident.

The section continues a little later with a night scene which provides final references to that particular hill scenery (not forgetting the trains yet again!). Presumably this was meant to be poetical, but of course it can be called literature only by courtesy of the very grossest exaggeration.

Very quietly they could hear a train roll past somewhere in the background.

'Yes; sometimes I've come down this way late at night, when I've been staying in the district on holiday and for all that have been up to town. Out of the dreary murk of London to speed away down the line towards here—and some time towards midnight, maybe, you get out at one of the smaller Downland stations. It's utterly dark and yet you soon realise there's a kind of silvery radiance behind or over everything; perhaps the moon's behind clouds and you get this unearthly effect. The Downs seem a ghostly range, with unreal valleys of interlocking spurs half visible as you walk along the road to where you're staying. In a few minutes, the hills work their effect on you, just as much as they do by day, but so differently; and you feel you've entered a new realm of reality where the memory of London is just a nightmare. The mental changeover from one atmosphere to the other is an amazing thing really.'

'I know what you mean. I've felt the same thing out at night on our marshes at home. But there's a tendency towards eerie loneliness there. You can't feel lonely with these gentle hills around, I think. And isn't it strange when an unseen cow or sheep moves behind a hedge as you're passing? Makes you feel you're intruding in a world which belongs all to the animals. And then you almost identify yourself with them! It's odd at our end; I don't know whether it's the same here. Some of the cows don't seem to go to sleep at all; they're still busily munching grass when I walk up from the last train at Famthorne sometimes. I suppose Barbara's Mary is still munching now, for that matter! And did you see the frightfully muddy hoof marks she left in the hall? I meant to help Barbara to sweep them up, but I forgot and she'll have done it by this time. Cows never will wipe their muddy boots — too much to expect! Oh, enough of the nonsense. I'm sure it's time to go in now.'

Another train sped by in the distance with a miniature rumble.

'Night train to the Downs,' she mused, half to herself. 'A fit subject for a poem, surely.'

Peter moved his arm around her more closely. 'It's a poem in itself to have you here in these beautiful surroundings.'

'That's just what I think about you too.' Her soft voice curled into the deepening dusk over the Weald before them. The groups of trees below the narrow foothill plateau on which the farm stood were shadowy now; a wispy mistiness was forming in the little valley to the left: the edges of the Downs would be softly mantled for the night.

Winifred sniffed the air appreciatively as they went in. The typical creamy flavor, so different from the thin, clear neutrality of her native east coast air, was particularly prominent.

Quite impossible by all standards, either then or now, as we can see perfectly well. But there it was. How or why, we cannot say. There may have been writings like this at the beginning of the twentieth century, but they were certainly very rare in the middle, to which this extraordinary specimen dates. We are entirely at a loss to account for it. It is almost more suitable for children than adults, but not actually even for them.

We shall certainly not waste our readers' time and patience by troubling to make any reference to the absurd plot itself and one or two sub-plots of this weird attempt at literary composition. We shall conclude our quotations with the no less typically extraordinary credo which is put in at the end of the book by way of a sort of quite impossible personal marriage compact. This successfully manages to muddle up in summary everything that went before.

We do not know why the world was made, nor why we are on it, but we believe it is the inescapable duty of every human being to find out as much as possible of the vast complexities of creation and to develop and retain an unfailing sense of wonder at the marvels of the universe. Curiosity is our first obligation.

We regard the next essential as being that of developing our own potentialities to the utmost and of using them to contribute something of advantage to the general progress of civilization. For this purpose, we regard cooperation as the essential basis of society and all competition for individualist material ends to be wicked. Consequently, we hold a socialist world state to be the only desirable form of suitable inclusive human organisation. All our political efforts must keep this ultimate end in view, it being unforgivable to take no action towards it.

The motive force and the basis of personal conduct working towards the ideal world must be an attitude of kindliness and respect in relation to all other men regardless of race, color, class, occupation, creed, or anything else; we are all of equal worth as human beings until we deliberately debase ourselves by ignoring our social responsibilities. The suffering of one is the suffering of all; evil is usually manmade and we must always aim at eliminating any which lies within our range of action. After music, education is the most important thing in life, for it alone enables us to formulate and carry out our ideals.

We believe in the overriding importance of the three oldtime rather inexplicable bases of satisfactory human happiness: truth, beauty, and goodness. It is possible that beauty is only an expression of comfort, founded on suitability for evolved characteristics, but it is also possible that it points beyond man himself to reflect higher realities yet beyond our ken. We find goodness to be permanently composed of kindliness, assistance towards ultimate human progress (whatever that may turn out to be) and a ruthless adherence to the truth, as far as we can ever know it, including a determination to penetrate as far as possible towards an understanding of ultimate reality. We consider sincerity to be the outward expression of inner honesty of thought.

We hold it particularly desirable to have at least some faint realisation of geological and astronomical time scales, if only as a corrective to overemphasis of petty, everyday affairs and as a suitable self-humbling mechanism before the wonders of creation, which, of course, include the marvel of man's own mind, although the latter may not be unique and can be expected to develop in at present inconceivable ways millions of years hence.

We attach profound importance to a sense of humor, considering it a vital necessity for everyone, recognising, however, that there are innumerable ways of manifesting it. The person who cannot sometimes do things for the sheer fun of being alive and playing around is quite inadequate.

We regard marriage as being based on a conscious drawing-together of ideals previously held separately in fairly close agreement, and we feel we shall gain the deepest satisfaction ourselves by dedicating our lives to the finest purposes we know beyond our mere personal desires.

And yet . . . And yet . . . Obviously there are really no words to comment on this entirely hopeless effort at serious literary writing – and apparently it actually was meant to be that. It is incompetent crudity from beginning to end. And in spite of all . . . there actually is something there. In its completely ineffective and incredibly clumsy way, it does point forward to some extent (which is, of course, one reason why we chose it). It was not quite right to use the word "hopeless" a few lines back. For if there is one thing in all this totally bad composition, it is just that – hope. Hope was the ingredient that was generally missing in twentieth century literature. With the rarest of exceptions, there was a constantly increasing decline into depression, decadence, pessimism, nihilism and, in the end, despair. Nothing so clearly evidences the decline of that civilization as this. It is true that towards the very end of the century, there was a certain improvement in approach as the world started to sort itself out, but by then it was natural, in accord with better circumstances and consequent outlook. This necessarily falls within the field of the historians of the following century to deal with.

Our readers will recollect that at the beginning of the extracts we have just presented, we requested them to reverse in spirit the substance and essence of these quotations, in order to gain a reasonably effective idea of the typical literature of a millenium ago. That request was meant seriously.

# 4 H. G. Wells—
## Prophet of the Century

The discerning reader, at least basically acquainted with ancient writing, will undoubtedly have noticed some slight reflection of the great prophet of the twentieth century, H. G. Wells, here and there in the "literary" excerpts given in the previous chapter. There can be no doubt that his influence shows itself here. It was a great influence indeed, and although there were many periods when it declined (including immediately after his own lifetime), Wells has necessarily become one of mankind's classics. It is impossible to treat the twentieth century in general historical fashion without taking him into account. Although his great work began in the nineteenth, he continued and developed it nearly all the first half of the twentieth, so it is to the latter that he really belongs. This is in spite of the fact that he has been called a typically English bourgeois Victorian. But he has been called many things, mostly wildly inaccurate because incompletely based. He was indeed a child of his time; even the most exceptional cannot totally escape that fate. However, he did escape it to the maximum possible degree, which is why he stands among the immortals. His fame as a prophet is not due to his foretelling of some future inventions and even happenings. This, if rare, is not by any means unique. Far from being merely farseeing, he manifested truly inspiring vision in the sense of implied moral guidance; he ultimately wears the mantle of prophet for reasons related to those applying to very ancient prophets of remote history.

Curiously enough, reviews and appraisals of Wells' work were very scanty in the twentieth century. He was taken seriously and appreciated at his true worth only in the twenty-first, when the upturn had well begun and a rational approach to mankind's problems began to get the upper hand. In the past several hundred years, there have been fresh appraisals from time to time, in accordance with the changing spirit of the age, as in the case of other great classics. His works have been freely available nearly everywhere, due to their directly universal character, and they remain a precious item in our cultural heritage. In spite of the production of still earlier utopian books (some outstanding classics in their own rights) the greatest of Wells' many writings stand as the first clear expression of the modern outlook, of man's free and brotherly flowering.

In these circumstances, we have no need to enter into exhaustive analysis afresh, but merely to make the necessary stress on the centrality of Wells' figure in our review-century and to show him as the outstanding revolutionary of the time in the biggest and best sense of that word. This is a justified assessment, although Wells (not only human but very human indeed) did make mistakes, mistakes in the way of unbalanced outlook and undoubted misjudgment in a few matters; it is not even sure that all these mistakes were unavoidable. A little more patience, a little more willingness to stand corrected on occasion, could have made the final account more completely impressive than it has acknowledgedly been for the last millenium. For instance, Wells was the complete world citizen at one blow, the total cosmopolitan. The purity of his vision in this respect cannot be challenged. It can be said to constitute the very essence of his greatness. But he never seemed to realize that man can but advance by stages. He was, of course, right in condemning nationalism, that deadly curse of his age. But it was actually an unrealistic exaggeration to condemn offhand, outright and immediately, all idea of nationality and to contend that no nation could play a part towards internationalism in truth, through federation to the final cosmopolis. Mankind cannot leap headlong to attainment of the ideal. Improvements can be made only in steps. Probably no revolution in history ever achieved even a quarter of its idealistic aims. It slipped back much of the way while still in the very process of revolt, and occasionally fell back more than all the way and turned out to be retrograde. Such are the consequences of man's mental structure. Wells, brilliant historian though he was, never came to realize this effectively, although criticism, more or less of this character, accompanied him throughout. He could listen if he wanted to, but it seems he did not usually want to. He can hardly have been held to have communicated with his generation, which is no doubt why he was remarkably ignored by both it and the next. There was a difficulty in that he was approved and applauded for the wrong things; or rather, not for wrong things but for less important ones. That he really could write literature (unlike that unknown author of our previous chapter) is and was obvious. Some of his portrayal of human character has remained notable throughout recent ages. But the united-world vision in his work was what finally mattered. This was definitely not generally appreciated in his time and just afterwards, and even later times have not invariably realized it adequately.

Wells made a total mistake about that very special people, the Jews, the link between the very ancient and ancient worlds, whose so-called Zionism in the end became an instrument for the attainment of his ideals, as he could logically have worked out if he had examined this idealism of theirs dispassionately on the basis of their being a world-dispersed people, linking all the national entities of his time. Being against particularism of every kind, in every way, he brushed Jewish particularism aside with the rest and entirely missed the point of its great potentialities in their case. He even went to the trouble of maligning them very carefully in more than one place in his writings, including *The Shape of Things to Come,* although this, his masterpiece has been regarded as the Bible of the century. But the greatest also have their blind spots, and this was certainly one of his. Such is the non-uniform structure of the human brain-field, even in the case of genius; all the more in the case of genius, some would say (this has not yet been finally proved). Nevertheless, one thing is indisputable: in spite of these and other mistakes the towering figure of Wells' genius stands, only very slightly impaired, among the supreme achievements of human thought. It is not that his detailed wording, his extensive planning of our planet, is in itself the totality of the matter. It is the general concepts which count: of all men as brothers, of our planet as a garden, of unceasing human adventure in simultaneous cooperation and freedom. This was the great vision of the prophet. And if there were misconceptions as well, they can be fully recognized and still taken for what they are: a small debit item in the marvellous account as a whole.

It should not be thought (although even now it sometimes still is) that Wells' output can be divided into novels on the one hand and social and scientific writings on the other. This is a common but grave mistake. Actually, a clear line of Wells' social thought runs through all his novels; his output was one and indivisible. In spite of exhaustive research, the present writer has not been able to trace any complete review of the development of this social thought of his chronologically through the novels. General reviews of it started to be written in the twentieth century itself, most notably by that finely critical Wellsian protagonist, W. Warren Wagar. But a full treatment of the novels themselves from this standpoint has not come to light. It may well be that there is still a place for it in our world's social history library. Anything of the sort, even on a miniature scale, is, of course, utterly out of the question here. Our readers need only a brief general view of essentials. That we can give by a few short extracts, choice examples taken from some of his finest work, directly or indirectly sociological in the end.

Our first specimen comes from one of his very latest novels, never a very well known one, the *Babes in the Darkling Wood* of 1940, a most unfairly neglected work, one of altogether remarkable quality. It must be admitted that the writing in this book is not very natural; it has a slightly forced effect. Perhaps this accounts for its lack of fame. Harking back to the last extract in the previous chapter, it is very appropriate that we should choose the lovers' "Memorandum," as Wells calls it in his novel. It very much looks as though there may have been a direct connection with Wells in the case of our second unidentified author, but there is some confusion of dates involved in the contexts and there is no certainty about it. At all events, the actual material is so different in particulars, in style and in weightiness, that the matter is of no consequence. Part of this memorandum, near the beginning, runs like this:

> . . . It is not true that the present moral, religious, political and social system is an inevitable, irreplaceable growth, in which the best thing to do politically is to manoeuvre about with treaties, leagues, Acts of Parliament and so forth, muddling along, staving things off. They all believe the present system is Necessity and Destiny. It is, they believe (and by this belief they are damned), the unavoidable Course of Events; the inevitable Thing that is. . . We deny all that. We refuse to take life at that, even if we are destroyed altogether for our refusal. . .
>
> We have agreed that in this gross, confused, moving and dangerous mass of a world as it is, there is hidden the possibility of a human existence of so general a happiness, such liveliness of interest and such abundance as no living species has ever yet known. Look at flowers, light in a thousand refractions, in sunsets, crystals, ripples, look at beautiful bodies, think of music, art, poetry — these are the mere first intimations of the

possibility of life as man might shape it. We believe that by a strenuous readjustment of mental and social life, a good, lovely and continually progressive world could be carved out of this enormous, dreadful world of today, as a sculptor carves loveliness out of his block.

This means that you and I are revolutionaries, to the fullest meaning of the word. That is to say we propose the abolition, supersession or reconstruction of every government, every social institution, every organisation in the world which keeps mankind divided and contentious, in favour of a single, rational and steadfastly progressive world system. Our world system includes not only governments but religion and, above all — education. We are against all these rulers and teachers as they exist, we are against them for the sake of our invincible belief in that possible new world. . . .we want to destroy nothing that can be made over into a new world. Much of the industrial life of the world, most production, can carry on, with a steady rationalisation, an increasing saturation of interest, efficiency and happiness. We simply want to change the spirit of the producer to a spirit of contented and interested world-citizenship.

For example, we do not want to destroy schools and teaching and the intelligence services of the world, press colleges, research institutions, etc., etc., but we want to expand, regenerate and invigorate them beyond measure, to give all these things concerned in mind-making, enormously greater powers and a vaster responsibility. Nor do we want, for example, to destroy the transport system of the world but to inject it with a broader conception of service. . . The great idea that has seized upon us can come to nothing unless it is an infectious idea and unless we contemplate new-world mechanical workers, new-world planters and plantation workers, new-world seamen and aviators, new-world medical services, etc., etc., all educated and accustomed to regard themselves primarily as owner-cooperators of the collective community. Their pride and their glory must be in their function. They must not attempt either to monopolise or possess. . .

The fundamental social crime . . . is *interception or appropriation* in *any* form. In *any* form whatever. It is a limited view that makes private property in matters of common interest, and the 'capitalist system,' the only social evils. There are many other conceivable forms of interception and monopolisation. Class

privilege or party rule or official authority or race discrimination
can intercept as badly or worse. The subtle variations of
interception or appropriation can be detected and controlled only
by the constant vigilance of an alert world public opinion. . .

And if we turn back nearly three decades in the Wellsian saga to the
also-neglected, very much earlier novel, *Marriage,* we find that already
in 1912 the course was fixed, although fewer details were available and
little more than the general aim was expressed. Probably overshadowed
by the very famous novels which had preceded it, this book is of no
slight beauty, revealing much insight into human nature. Towards the
end, a husband and wife who had drifted into misunderstanding in
ancient London go to the snows of Labrador to find each other afresh
amid adventures there, fully fitted up with a forward-looking world
outlook. Most of a short interlude in the Labradorian part of the story
goes like this:

What are we doing with life?
That question overtakes a reluctant and fugitive humanity.
The Traffords were but two of a great scattered host of people,
who, obeying all the urgencies of need and desire, struggling,
loving, begetting, enjoying, do nevertheless find themselves at last
unsatisfied. They have lived the round of experience, achieved all
that living creatures have sought since the beginning of the
world — security and gratification and offspring — and they find
themselves still strong, unsatiated, with power in their hands and
years before them, empty of purpose. What are they to do?
The world presents such a spectacle of evasion as it has never
seen before. Never was there such a boiling over and waste of vital
energy. The Sphinx of our opportunity calls for the uttermost
powers of heart and brain to read its riddle — the new, astonishing riddle of excessive power. A few give themselves to those
honourable adventures that extend the range of man, they
explore untravelled countries, climb remote mountains, conduct
researches, risk life and limb in the fantastic experiments of
flight, and a monstrous outpouring of labour and material goes on
in the strenuous preparation for needless and improbable wars. The
rest divert themselves with the dwarfish satisfaction of recognised
vice, the meagre routine of pleasure, or still more timidly with sport
and games—those new unscheduled perversions of the soul.

> We are afraid of our new selves. The dawn of human
> opportunity appals us. Few of us dare look upon this strange light
> of freedom and limitless resources that breaks upon our world.

This was written somewhat before the First World War, after which mankind proceeded straight along with no basic change to the Second World War (only the atomic threat of substantially total destruction preserved it from a third). Although basic change did start in the Eastern Bloc only five years after *Marriage* was published, it took a very long time to bring experimentation to something better; the demands of the prophet were not satisfied.

For a few choice final specimens, we naturally turn to the specifically sociological works. A highly important point extensively treated in that most significant *A Modern Utopia* is the question of "samurai," trained leaders of men. Since Wells wrote (at the beginning of the twentieth century) civilization has brought up many varieties of this idea in practice, and of course it existed in at least as many varieties in previous history, taking on various forms of elite often greatly contrasted with the ancient Japanese model. This matter belongs rather to our next chapter on politics, and it will be sufficient to say here that our current tendency being to keep our democracy as cooperatively equalitarian as possible, there has been no recent usage of samurai in the modern world. The matter will probably be brought up again at no very distant annual World Discussion, as there is periodically felt a need for a source of fresh, additional stimulation, inspiration, general polishing up of human activity, and the samurai system does seem to be able to provide that extra push from time to time. At present, it is not generally considered to be a permanently needed feature of civilization. All elites except the natural intellectual one have long since been eliminated in the field of social power. For the past century or two there has been evidence of a widespread distaste for reintroducing a philosophical one. It is possible that at long last we have outgrown the need for anything of the sort, leadership being so broadly, evenly diffused throughout the world community. But this has yet to come up for discussion at least once more; we cannot say the idea is dead yet. Perhaps it may never be.

Back in 1905, Wells was writing philosophically rather than politically. The vague earlier ideals of the prophet had not yet crystallized very much. (They never did to a final degree, and that is at one and the same time a strength and a weakness of the great thinker.) The philosophical presentation of the samurai concept in *A Modern Utopia* is a lengthy business, so we shall reproduce only the central, more dramatic section, and have no hesitation in referring readers back to this valuable classic for the rest, and, we hope, the remainder of the book as well.

For seven consecutive days in the year, at least, each man or woman under the Rule must go right out of all the life of man into some wild and solitary place, must speak to no man or woman, and have no sort of intercourse with mankind. They must go bookless and weaponless, without pen or paper, or money. Provisions must be taken for the period of the journey, a rug or sleeping sack — for they must sleep under the open sky — but no means of making a fire. They may study maps beforehand to guide them, showing any difficulties and dangers in the journey, but they may not carry such helps. They must not go by beaten ways or wherever there are inhabited houses, but into the bare, quiet places of the globe — the regions set apart for them.

This discipline . . . was invented to secure a certain stoutness of heart and body in the members of the Order, which otherwise might have lain open to too many timorous, merely abstemious, men and women. Many things had been suggested, swordplay and tests that verged on torture, climbing in giddy places and the like, before this was chosen. Partly, it is to ensure good training and sturdiness of body and mind, but partly, also, it is to draw their minds for a space from the insistent details of life, from the intricate arguments and the fretting effort to work, from personal quarrels and personal affections, and the things of the heated room. Out they must go, clean out of the world.

Certain great areas are set apart for these yearly pilgrimages beyond the securities of the State. There are thousands of square miles of sandy desert in Africa and Asia set apart; much of the Arctic and Antarctic circles; vast areas of mountain land and frozen marsh; secluded reserves of forest, and innumerable unfrequented lines upon the sea. Some are dangerous and laborious routes; some merely desolate; and there are even some sea journeys that one may take in the halcyon days as one drifts through a dream. Upon the seas one must go in a little undecked sailing boat, that may be rowed in a calm; all the other journeys one must do afoot, none aiding. There are, about all these desert regions and along most coasts, little offices at which the samurai says goodbye to the world of men, and at which they arrive after their minimum time of silence is overpast. For the intervening days they must be alone with Nature, necessity, and their own thoughts. . .

'I don't sleep much at nights on these journeys; I lie awake and stare at the stars. About dawn, perhaps, and in the morning sunshine, I sleep! The nights this last time were very short, never more than twilight, and I saw the glow of the sun always, just over the edge of the world. But I had chosen the days of the new moon, so that I could have a glimpse of the stars . . . Years ago, I went from the Nile across the Libyan Desert east, and then the stars – the stars in the later days of that journey –brought me near weeping. You begin to feel alone on the third day, when you find yourself out on some shiny snowfield, and nothing of mankind visible in the whole world save one landmark, one remote thin red triangle of iron, perhaps, in the saddle of the ridge against the sky. All this busy world that has done so much and so marvellously, and is still so little – you see it as it is – and far off. All day long you go and the night comes, and it might be another planet. Then, in the quiet, waking hours, one thinks of one's self and the great external things, of space and eternity, and what one means by God . . . when I go among snows and desolations – and usually I take my pilgrimage in mountains or the north – I think very much of the Night of this World – the time when our sun will be red and dull, and air and water will lie frozen together in a common snowfield where now the forests of the tropics are steaming. . . I think very much of that, and wheth-er it is indeed God's purpose that our kind should end, and the cities we have built, the books we have written, all that we have given substance and a form, should lie dead beneath the snows. I went threading my way among gorges and precipices, with my poor brain dreaming of what the alternative should be, with my imagination straining and failing. Yet, in those high airs and in such solitude, a kind of exaltation comes to men. . . I remember that one night I sat up and told the rascal stars very earnestly how they should not escape us in the end.'

That mention of the Night of the World reminds one of the sustained drama of the conclusion of *The Time Machine,* dating back ten years earlier. It would indeed be superfluous to quote from this vividly surviving classic; everyone normally versed in world literature knows how the stamp of literary greatness lies on Wells' best writing, apart from the much greater greatness of his world-oriented human vision. But we are reminded of the conclusion of the masterwork of Wells' contemporary, Olaf Stapledon, *Last and First Men,* to which we made a previous reference. When he imagines the last of the Last Men, Stapledon chooses a heat death instead of a cold death for our planet, and closes truly beautifully in a manner that challenges even Wells in his most artistic moments:

> But one thing is certain. Man himself, at the very least, is music, a brave theme that makes music also of its vast accompaniment, its matrix of storms and stars. Man himself in his degree is eternally a beauty in the eternal form of things. It is very good to have been man. And so we may go forward together with laughter in our hearts, and peace, thankful for the past, and for our own courage. For we shall make after all a fair conclusion to this brief music that is man.
> we shall make after all a fair conclusion to this brief music that is man.

We must conclude our quotations from Wells himself, though, and cannot avoid jumping forward to his own masterpiece, *The Shape of Things to Come,* which preceded the Second World War by only six years. The vision in full force, and so beautifully written too: the "Declaration of Mégève:"

> The World-State now follows all the subordinate states it swallowed up to extinction; the supreme sovereign government, which conquered and absorbed all minor sovereignties, vanishes from human affairs. The long, and often blind and misdirected, effort of our race for peace and security has at length succeeded, thanks to this great Council that now retires. It retires with the applause and gratitude of all mankind. And now in serenity and security we can survey the property it has redeemed from waste, this planet and its possibilities, our own undeveloped possibilities too, and all the fullness of life that lies before us. This is the day,

this is the hour of sunrise for united manhood. The Martyrdom of Man is at an end. From pole to pole now there remains no single human being upon the planet without a fair prospect of self-fulfilment, of health, interest and freedom. There are no slaves any longer; no poor; none doomed by birth to an inferior status; none sentenced to long unhelpful terms of imprisonment; none afflicted in mind or body who are not being helped with all the powers of science and the services of interested and able guardians. The world is all before us to do with as we will, within the measure of our powers and imaginations. The struggle for material existence is over. It has been won. The need for repressions and disciplines has passed. The struggle for truth and that indescribable necessity which is beauty begins now, unhampered by any of the imperatives of the lower struggle. No one now need live less nor be less than his utmost.

We must respect the race and each other, but that has been made easy for us by our upbringing. We must be loyal to the conventions of money, of open witness, of responsibility for the public peace and health and decency: these are the common obligations of the citizen by which the commonweal is sustained. We must contribute our modicum of work to the satisfaction of the world's needs. And, for the rest, now *we can live.* No part of the world, no work in the world, no pleasure, except such pleasure as may injure others, is denied us. . .

And afterwards:

As the curtain of separatist dreams, racial fantasies and hate nightmares thinned out and passed away, what was presented to that awakening human brain? A little sunlit planet, for its external material, bearing what we now realise is not a tithe of its possible flora and fauna, a ball crammed with unused and unsuspected resources; and for the internal stuff of that brain almost limitless possibilities of mental achievement. All that had been done hitherto by man was like the scribbling of a little child before eye and hand have learnt sufficient coordination to draw. It was like the pawing and crawling of a kitten before it begins to see. And now man's eyes were open.

Extensive quotation from this noble work is naturally not necessary: after all, it is one of humanity's standard textbooks. We but remind our readers of some main points, worth emphasizing to accord with the main line we are taking for our twentieth century review. On this latter account, it would not be ideally appropriate to reproduce the book's final words, for they relate back to the samurai-elite concept of three decades earlier which we today are inclined to regard as one of Well's mistakes, however beautifully expressed. Just before the end, though, readers will remember these famous phrases:

> Our sense of our individual difference makes our realisation of our common being more acute. We work, we think, we explore, we dispute, we take risks and suffer — for there seems no end to the difficult and dangerous adventures individual men and women may attempt; and more and more plain does it become to us that it is not our little selves, but Man the Undying who achieves these things through us.

Slightly before that comes the summing-up passage which makes the clearest conclusion in our present context:

> ... Well over ninety per cent of the human population was absorbed either in the direct production of necessities or in the scramble to get them from their original producers. Direct producers, the peasants and toilers, the entrepreneurs and their managers and directors, and direct distributors accounted for upward of eighty per cent of the human total; the rest were the millions of interveners, usurers, claim-makers, landowners, rentiers, solicitors, speculators, parasites, robbers, and thieves, who were deemed necessary to ginger up the economic process. The forces of law, order and education, excluding temporary conscription and levies for military ends, took up five or six per cent of the residue, and a small minority, something under five per cent of the total population, supplied all the artistic effort, the scientific enquiry, the social and political thought, the living soul of the entire social body.

> The systems of interest of most people were therefore restricted almost entirely to work and the struggle to possess. They had to think continually of the work they did either for their

own profit or for the personal profit, comfort or fantasy of some
employer. They had to think of keeping their jobs or of getting
fresh ones, and this, in the days of narrowing employment after
the Hoover Slump, became at last a monstrous obsession of the
brain. What they earned they had to spend carefully or guard
carefully, for the rascaldom of business was everywhere seeking
to give nothing for something. Sometimes, sick of their narrow
lives, they would gamble in the desperate hope of a convulsive
enlargement, and for most of them gambling meant disappoint-
ment and self-reproach. Add to these worries a little love, a good
deal of hate, and a desperate struggle to see it all in a hopeful and
honourable light, a desperate hunger to be flattered and reas-
sured, and you have the content of ninety nine per cent of the
human brains that made the world of 1930. They could no more
escape from this restricted circle of urgently clamorous interests,
hardly ampler than the circle of an animal's interest, than the
animals can.

The Modern State has broken this cramping circle of interests
for every human being. We are still creatures with brains like our
forefathers, corresponding ganglia to ganglia and fibre to fibre,
but *we are not using those brains for the same purposes.* The
Modern State, by ensuring plenty and controlling the increase of
population, has taken all the interests of the food-hunt and the
food-scramble, and all the interests of the struggle to down-and-
out our human competitors, away from the activities of the individual brain. A relatively small number of specialised workers
keep the necessary Controls of these primary preoccupations
going. We worry about food, drink, clothing, health and personal
freedom no more. The work we *must* do is not burthensome in
amount, and it is the most congenial our educational guardians
can find for us and help us to find. When it is done we are sure of
the result; nobody is left in the world to cheat us or rob us of our
pay. We are still competitive, more so perhaps than ever; jealousy
still wars with generosity in us; the story of our personal affections is rarely a simple story; but the interest we feel in our work
is a masterful interest and not a driven interest, and our competition is for distinction, appreciation and self-approval, and not for
mutal injury. There has been a release of by far the larger moiety
of the mental energy of the normal man from its former inescapable preoccupations.

In true prophetic style, Wells undoubtedly knew how to hit hard!

But that is not our very last Wellsian excerpt. The final one, brief as it is, is the most apt of all. It refers to Wells' "Open Conspiracy" concept, his famous, once more samurai-like idea, that those who see the light, the chosen ones, can gradually get together round the world and quite openly organize and carry out the final liberating revolution. He was always against yet another political movement; so how he believed this could be done has never been entirely clear. Ancient correspondence shows that he tended to take refuge in vagueness, to say the time was not yet ripe and to advise waiting. When it came to it, he retreated, apparently, from the partially concrete action programs suggested in his "Open Conspiracy" books; he did go so far as to mention a definite movement in them. We have not hesitated to critize Wells adversely on occasion above, and we do not now either. But, so as to leave the last word with the grand old prophet himself, we should like to much more than counter this with our own summing-up at this point.

Mistakes and all, Wells was one of the few who could project himself forward out of his century with unforgettably inspiring results; this in spite of his formulations inevitably bearing the stamp of his time. His expressed ideals for mankind were not devoid of the stamp of immortality as well. For the most part, they were in the loftiest line of altruistic thought. Not even in his own time did anyone deny that Wells, a man who refused public honors, stood in solid sympathy for the rights of the common man, as well as for the Rights of Man. It is certainly not only the huge quantity of his magnificent output which impresses, but the sheer quality of its much more limited peak points in the visionary field. It is these which are most fitted for comparison with the greatest works of Teilhard de Chardin, Stapledon, and very few other thinkers of the twentieth century; there is no doubt in the modern world that, fully admitting the greatness of these others in opening up vital new mental vistas in their time, it was Wells, with his grasp of man's social future, who wore the actual prophet's mantle of a thousand years past.

The closing paragraph of his *What Are We to Do With Our Lives?* reads:

> The Open Conspiracy is the awaking of mankind from a nightmare, an infantile nightmare, of the struggle for existence and the inevitability of war. The light of day thrusts between our eyelids,

and the multitudinous sounds of morning clamour in our ears. A time will come when men will sit with history before them or with some old newspaper before them and ask incredulously, 'Was there ever such a world?'

Which is, of course, exactly what our readers do do today.

# 5 The Political Position

Politics is the art of living in community. Other definitions are possible; but this one will serve us sufficiently. It is amusing to think that in those strange islands of Britain (to which we have alluded several times already), it was generally considered "not the thing" to talk about politics at all! It simply was "not done" among many of the middle range of that unusual society. Political talk was quite the fashion in aristocratic circles, but it was done in a narrow, academic, professional manner, descended from previous centuries. Also, politics did enter into the conversation of the historically famous British "working class", but was kept within the artificial limits of superficial trade union considerations almost entirely. (The worker's organizations, called trade unions, were an integral part of "The Establishment" — the personnel of the directorate of the established social order in those times — although they had, in some instances at least, been intended to serve comparatively revolutionary aims.) This was an extreme case, due to the abnormally secure, long-term semi-isolation of Britain in the preceding era. The local community lived automatically, one could say; a habit directly descended from its feudal days when every person had his fixed place in society and only the powerful lords operated the political art. But it will serve as a pointed introduction to show the prevailing artificiality of politics in that century.

Not even on the adjacent Europian continent were politics usually taken for granted in any such manner, as surviving newspapers clearly evidence. Western political democracy there, as the multiplicity of parties showed, was much more dynamic in tendency, but was still unreal from the modern point of view. In the Eastern Bloc, trade unions were part of the governmental apparatus, and the position, although revolutionized, remained generally static. From our standpoint today, politics are not politics if they are not dynamic, vividly felt, lived and acted directly, personally by everyone. But this was scarcely ever the case in the ancient world. The art of living in community was prostituted into a mere technique of living in community, ready-ordered from above, the British example being surely the most extreme instance of all (apart, of course, from actually dictatorial regimes, all too common in that sad century). Politics were made the profession of the few, a technical career in itself. Such an absurdity, considering that politics are obviously fundamental in normal, healthy, personal, daily life, is incredible to us in our happier era. But so it was; and in this, perhaps we have already made our main point. In the actual East and the undeveloped part of the world in general, politics were either on a local, tribal level, usually feudal, occasionally democratic; or they were dictatorial, until Western Bloc modernization came into the picture through economic spread. They then took on a form similar to that we already mentioned: nominally popular, but in fact more dead than alive. In those times, of course, our remarks would have been indignantly repudiated as grossly unfair and an incorrect interpretation of the position. Nowadays, though, researchers are rarely to be found differing from this standpoint in any marked degree.

A handful of contemporary quotations will help to prove our point. They will show that the basic evil of the then current inadequacy was occasionally recognized by responsible thinkers aware enough to realize the situation, although they were caught up in its socio-mental tentacles themselves. For instance, there was a praiseworthy American socioligist named McIver, who, in his book *Society,* wrote thus:

> The individual who slavishly follows the nearest code is unconscious of or unfitted for a greater social obligation. For him, society lies without; it has no deep roots within his being. He is bound to it by the superficial and uncreative bonds of imitation and compliance. He reflects but does not express society; for him it is not *community.* No human being is in fact so pure an embodiment of the herd spirit. The primitive savage has been so pictured . . . but more recent anthropology has undermined 'the assumption that in primitive societies the individual is completely dominated by the group —the horde, the clan or the tribe — that he obeys the commands of his community, its traditions, its public opinion, its decrees, with a slavish, fascinated, passive obedience.' What needs further to be observed is that this spirit of

passive obedience, to which of course we find approximations both in civilized and in primitive society, especially in matters of belief, is the least and not the most fully developed expression of social-mindedness. To be fully social is to be socially *responsible,* to bring the whole social situation, as it affects and is affected by one's conduct, into the focus of one's consciousness and act accordingly. This however is a statement of the ideal, to which in actuality we find only various degrees of approximation.

Exactly — and magnificent! Our applause and that of our readers is necessarily unrestrained. That such a statement could come from twentieth century North America again seems unbelievable, but as we have exemplified several times previously, it was not entirely exceptional, though comparatively rare. It may be that the primitive savage retained some independence of outlook, i.e. had some individual political thought in effect, but certainly little of this remained among the commercially brain-washed Western poeple at their worst, a situation which became all too universal in the end. If only perspicacious analyses could have been translated into action! So much waste, suffering, and tragedy could have been averted, for the scientific techniques, limited though they were, were sufficient to enable mankind to go forward fairly successfully. But it was not to be; the moral drive was not there. It had been undermined by the deadly commercial materialism of the West that spread East. That civilization did go down the drain, and only in the next century could human values flourish freely once more.

Even at the beginning of the twentieth century, ultimate political ideals in society were already well expressed, as the next quotation indicates. This was true of various earlier ages, too; but the twentieth century, with its relatively developed applied science was the first era which could actually have put these ideals into practice. It is this which is the essence of the tragedy. Practical possibilities were not taken up, although they could have been. Politics were never made an effective reality in the living, communal sense (except in one or two special corners of the world, on all too small a scale, to which we shall inevitably refer specifically at the end). The cause was that fatal absence of the essential underlying morality, that basic requirement so effectually killed by the successfully self-advertising business men on the one side and no less successfully self-advertising dictatorial leaders on the other. Both were no doubt well-meaning, with the best of educational intentions, but, alas, hopelessly misguided.

Our relevant quotation this time is taken from a book of 1918, *The Metaphysical Theory of the State,* by L. T. Hobhouse:

> ... with political education and the development of effective democracy the sphere of intelligent social control is extended, and it would be a sound statement of the democratic ideal to say that it conceives a possible society regulating its common life by common consent, in which a larger and larger porportion of its members actively participate until a position be reached in which society would control itself as simply and effectively as the individual controls himself. This is an ideal and not one very near to realisation. Of the social structure of any state that exists it is generally untrue to say that it is clearly conceived by the minds of the majority of those who live in it. ... The actual institutions of society have been in large measure determined by class conflicts, struggles of churches, racial wars, and everywhere there are the marks of the struggles. ..

Quite so. Let us also quote Bergson, on similar lines, in his *The Two Sources of Morality and Religion:*

> It is easy, then, to understand that humanity should have arrived at democracy as a later development (for they were false democracies, those cities of antiquity, based on slavery, relieved by this fundamental iniquity of the biggest and most excruciating problems). Of all political systems, it is indeed the furthest removed from nature, the only one to transcend, at least in intention, the conditions of the "closed society." It confers on man inviolable rights. These rights, in order to remain inviolate, demand of all men an incorruptible fidelity to duty. It therefore takes for its matter an ideal man, who respects other as he does himself, inserting himself into obligations which he holds to be absolute, so that it is no longer possible to say whether it is the duty that confers the right or the right which imposes the duty. The citizen thus defined is both 'law-maker and subject,' as Kant has it. The citizens as a whole, the people, are therefore sovereign. Such is democracy in theory. It proclaims liberty, demands equality, and reconciles these two hostile sisters by reminding them that they are sisters, by exalting above everything fraternity. Looked at from this angle, the republican motto shows that the

third term dispels the oft-noted contradiction between the two others, and that the essential thing is fraternity: a fact which would make it possible to say that democracy is evangelical in essence and that its motive power is love.

The basis of and for politics is most strikingly expressed by Leonard Woolf in his book, *Barbarians at the Gate,* which dates back to the period of the Second World War:

> What are the essential elements in civilised life and how in fact are they created, preserved and destroyed? The three main factors which determine the nature of all social life and on which, therefore, the preservation or destruction of civilisation depends, are power, economics, and ideas. The politician who acts on the assumption that any one of these three elements is of decisive importance and that the others can be neglected will ultimately end in disaster, and political theories which pursue the same course end by becoming dogmatic phantasies. The difference between civilisation and barbarism consists of a difference in social relations, in the relation of the individuals to one another and to the community. These relations are affected by the use and distribution of power, by the economic structure, and by the social objectives and standards of social value pursued by those who control power. The three factors do not each operate upon society in a vacuum of its own; they are closely articulated and inter-connected. At one moment a change in the economic structure may initiate a process leading to a change in the control of power and therefore of social objectives and standards of value; at another a change in the control of power, e.g. a revolution, may lead to a change in the economic system and therefore of social ideas or ideals; at another mass conversion to the pursuit of a particular social ideal may produce a redistribution of power and change both the economic system and the relations of individuals to one another and to the community.

Disagreement on details exists today as it did then, and probably always will in a live, progressive society. But the difference between those remote times and our own is that the disagreement then was not merely on details: it was on fundamentals. This reached its extreme expression in the renowned East-West ideological clash to which we must shortly refer; but, for that matter, there was, no more than partial agreement on fundamentals on both sides of the clash alike. Neither side was really clear about its own political fundamentals. Perhaps this was just as well in one way, for it gave the opportunity, in the course of time, for each side to borrow from the other, and, in the very, very long run, to unite the world in an integrated political system through a process of gradually increasing federation. But the childishness of it all appalls us today. Harold Laski, whom we quoted previously, said at the time, "In no age are fundamental questions raised save where the body politic is diseased." The body politic was indeed never so diseased as in the period under review. He also said, "In practice, emotion, not intellect, rules." Also too terribly true. In fact, the notable early North American sociologist, Lester F. Ward, stressed this very point at the beginning of his *Dynamic Sociology* written at the end of the nineteenth century. Unless we can progress much further with our electrical brain control methods, this is likely always to remain true. But we have long reached the stage of letting the intellect have an appreciable share in the proceedings, and have consequently attained a reasonable basis for organization and action. A thousand years ago, on the other hand, it appears that emotion reigned nearly supreme, and the reasoned statements we have quoted stood no change of coming to the fore in practice.

The most extraordinary beliefs were current at that sorry time. One such was that different forms of government were suited to different peoples with their different histories. Of course, this is fundamentally absurd, since all men, being human, have common needs, so why ever should different types of government be called for? To cover stages of transition from widespread temporary illiteracy or other temporary lack of general standards, or for local climatic or other "technical" reasons, only moderate convenient variants of the basic type need be employed. But at that time mankind was ludicrously split into separate groups, their effective federation having hardly begun. There was still a strong tendency to invent artificial differences, just to keep the groups even further apart than was at all necessary for such reasons as securing local cultures, for instance. (It is quite true that different genes and consequent different brain currents prevailed in different peoples, as they still do today. But the mixture is ever increasing, and we are steadily developing measures of scientific control, so as to avoid agressive differentiation.) In that period, with reason at a discount and blind emotion prodominant (as was most evident in the nationalist field), matters were commonly made worse than they need have been, instead of better. The amazing position was reached in which politicians became a curse instead of a blessing. This naturally made them despised. Politics were commonly condemned as a dirty business, and society calmly cut the ground from under its feet by dissociating itself from its own ideological basis! Inevitably its atomization proceeded apace. The individual felt no responsibility to anyone beyond his own family; at the worst, political talk was ruled out of court altogether. That such self-defeating behavior could but end in collapse was made less evident by sheer force of social inertia; automatically deceptive blindness to the facts of the situation prevailed for a long period. In the Eastern Bloc, as opposed to the Western, politics were imposed on the people from above. While theoretically better than having no politics at all among the body of the people, it was naturally insecurely based and ran into all manner of practical difficulties. Only in the long run was political education finally successful there, and then it turned out to be largely wrong. So a further long period of revision had to ensue. It was a very painful social process indeed. But it was at least a conscious process, although often misdirected.

The question of education for democracy was never tackled successfully at that time. Democracy could not work because the people were too uneducated to be able to participate. It was not only that they had no actual political education, or perhaps some of the wrong sort; the masses everywhere had insufficient education altogether. They had no clear conceptions of local or world affairs on either the scientific or artistic sides, let alone a moderate combined culture of both, except in the case of the upper few per cent mentioned in one of our excerpts from H. G. Wells. The position was considerably improved mid-century, under the stimulus of vigorous progress in the Eastern Bloc in addition to a slower, indigenous improvement in the Western one. But it did little good, as almost all politics had a generally bad name by then. It was a recognized vested interest of the politicians, who were primarily concerned with keeping the public out of it instead of educating them into it. In Western parliamentary democracy politicans were at the same time dependent upon the votes of the populace; so one can easily understand how insincere and artificial the whole procedure soon became. Much of politics was a pack of lies from beginning to end. Part of it, on the other hand, was a genuinely sincere attempt to meet public requirements honestly. But this part stood little chance of winning the day, and rarely did. The division between "we" and "they" was too great; in spite of serious organizational efforts here and there, governors and governed were much too far apart for any real good to be done. In the Eastern Bloc, although the matter was carefully organized in theory, the gulf was commonly even greater still. This great divergence between theory and practice received much attention at the time and ever afterwards; it has perhaps never been entirely satisfactorily worked out. Various conflicting local conditions came into play to produce these disappointing results. The question is an extremely involved one into which we cannot enter here, and can only recommend interested readers to look up the relevant specialist studies on the subject.

The failure of Western democracy (as it was then) was due to the opportunist strategy inevitably replacing moral purpose. To gain the votes of the people, one had to indulge in endless tactical considerations, which prevented one from putting through fine public programs. The system, for this simple reason, was basically unworkable in any full and deep sense. All it could do was to keep society ticking over with varying degrees of uneasiness. In the few best Welfare States, of relatively high general education standards, a modest, although never complete, success was actually achieved, representing then Western civilization at its highest point. Elsewhere, the position was infinitely inferior. At the worst, everyone with social power tried to grab the political machine for his own interests and those of his group. If a fairly decent balance emerged (and it was always pretended, quite dishonestly, that one did), that was sheer good luck. For society was competitive in groups, as well as between individuals, and democracy in the deepest sense cannot work in such circumstances.

Among the curious political beliefs of the Western Bloc at the time was the insistence that one cannot have democracy without a parliamentary opposition. This was a very well-intentioned safeguard against dictatorship, but it strikes us as comical, even if we concede that it almost had some justification in the primitive circumstances of the age. What was indeed comical was that it became a basic principle in itself —clearly a superfluity. Obviously, if a people is going in a certain direction, it does not need to pull itself back every few years by changing over, for no good reason at all, to an opposite direction. Sustained progress is impossible in such contradictory conditions. Constant criticism is indeed vital; but even if one is maintaining a party system at all (far from essential in the long run once society is rationally organized), a machinery of intensive criticism can be worked out with no great difficulty within the framework of one party. In practice it was. But the fact was carefully denied! Political parties developed strongly divergent wings. Splinter parties, or minor parties only variants on main ones, arose. All this was quite effective criticism within one general party line, causing the line to vary according to need from time to time. But no one admitted it! Irrational, non-factual doctrinairism held such sway over those poor fettered minds. In the west an artificial system of two main parties developed, or at any rate two main groups of partially associated parties, and political energies were very largely wasted on the mock-battle between them. In the Anglo-Saxon lands of those times, the two main "opposing" parties eventually became nearly indistinguishable, except on a few old theoretical stands which were of little practical account. There was broad general agreement on the national policy line concerned. and this line was fairly well adhered to, whatever label it might be advertised under during any particular year. This fact became clear to all in the end, and the knowledge served to increase apathy and disrespect for politics. Politics, which should have been the mental life-blood of the people, became a game; but a game heavily imbued with power implications — an all-too-serious sport, in fact, out of touch with the real needs of those affected by it.

The party system originally reflected the ideologies, based on actual needs, of social classes. In time, however, in certain regions, class lines became blurred, and party ones did too. Propaganda sometimes succeeded in persuading people to vote out of their class, against their own interests. As this tendency grew, it became a great social victory for the politicians in power. "Party" became a world social habit. So when the political Easterners came to power, they retained this habit as a social management and education tool, for which purpose it was indeed very useful. However, they needed only one party, so this system became known as the one-party system. More precisely it was simply a government with an apparatus for securing public support attached to it, the whole thing being diffused among the people (although hopelessly inefficiently and ineffectually in the earlier days of centralization, until its opposite was finally seen to be essential). In spite of its title, it had nothing to do with real political parties, originally based on class interests and principles. Westerners had no need to condemn a *genuine* one-party system as dictatorship. It would be nothing of the sort. As a matter of fact, they virtually had it themselves in such instances as we have mentioned, but made a pretense split-up of it, either for controlling the public more amenably, or for old times' sake; we are a little baffled by the whole phenomenon by this time. A genuine one-party system in a representative democracy would be a quite convenient method of reasonable public control-machinery, far preferable to uneasy coalition governments or disguised one-party systems. There was not the slightest need to condemn it in its pure form. On the contrary. But they always did. Such was the artificiality of thought, imposed from above.

The Eastern nomenclature undoubtedly deceived them too. If that is one-party rule, we do not want it, they could reasonably say. But it was not one-party rule. It was no-party rule. It was just governmental rule, except insofar as local soviets and suchlike moderated it by direct democracy in some cases. Intermediate forms of indirect democracy also moderated it in others. Not only was democracy not generally democracy by way of self-rule in the East then, but the Eastern Bloc "party" was not a political party in the Western sense. It was primarily a means of putting things across: a propagandist agency. There is much difference between a propaganda agency for political education with a governing directorate, on the one hand, and an elected set of representatives with their propaganda branch on the other. It was absurd to confuse them, but they managed to do so very well. A political party, we must insist, is strictly a piece of the *representative* government machinery of indirect democracy. The elected representatives of the people form themselves into one or more parties, thereby giving themselves effective political power (elections were originally for persons, in the earliest times, not for parties) — administrative organizations with public propaganda branches. A political party is not, as the Easterners made it by misuse of the term, a propagandist apparatus, however necessary, justified and good in its aims and results, with a nominated central governing group directing it and administering the community through it. It does not make the slightest difference if the leaders of the propagandist organization are "broken off" and put in the governing positions or if some of the govenors are given prominent propagandist functions. All this has nothing to do with representative government through a party apparatus, singular or plural, for it is not representative government at all. (That the "representativeness" of such a government is highly imaginary to a marked degree is true; nevertheless, it does represent to some extent certain public interests, mostly far too sectional, of course.) It is simply government through nominated officials. Public endorsement through ostensibly Western style elections may be of no small educative value, but is not exactly of practical reality or significance. Later on, this Eastern system did develop into something like what we have now, a representative kind of government without our calling any part of the machinery a party in any case. But ours is so truly representative and there are so many self-governing direct elements in the mechanism that there are no real grounds for comparison with either East or West in those far-off days. It is an altogether more advanced structure. Its roots were establishing themselves in the twentieth century, but struggled in a mass of hopelessly distorted vested interest pressures in the West and very real social organization difficulties in the East.

The reader will realize that, in effect, we have already been dealing with some of the essence of the great collision between the two Blocs which had such grave effects on twentieth century civilization. Something of the clashing ideologies has been mentioned, and prominence given to the confusion and misconception involved. Such mistakes pervaded the whole affair. The constant misunderstanding nearly makes one think the whole quarrel between Eastern and Western politicians was no more than a giant mistake. This is not quite true; but there is more in it than most people imagined at the time. We can arrive at this conclusion with no little backing from analysis of the unending newspaper reports of the time devoted to the subject; the annoyed articles, countercharges and refutations, often descending to absurd childishness. Both the Eastern and the Western Bloc societies were planned economies (in different ways), giant technological concerns, both of which called themselves democracies in ludicrously diverse interpretations of the term, and neither getting anywhere near final and complete democracy in that century.

The Western pattern of democracy gave power over the people to their representatives, who exerted their every effort to disguise the fact and were indeed dependent on public opinion to the extent that they succeeded or failed in these efforts and exertions. The Eastern pattern practically ignored such indirect democracy, made limited experiments with direct democracy on occasion, substituted State capitalism for private capitalism, had the greatest difficulty in later incorporating some Western elements back again, called the uncertain result Communism, by way of political title, to which ideology it bore approximately no relationship whatever (as they admitted when analyzing seriously), and sailed into smoother political waters only towards the end of the century. By that time, the Russo-Chinese split had had the effect of bringing Russia nearer to the West. When the Chinese planners finally succeeded in modernizing their vast region and bringing it into a position of world predominance, it was already the twenty-first century. Everyone was ready to quiet down politically (science and technology no longer left open even the partial alternative which still persisted most of the twentieth). They then found, to their surprise, that the gaps between their outlooks had dwindled to such an extent that it was possible to start organizing the world seriously for the first time in history. But that is outside our period for review, and the details are all in the history books.

Was there a real argument between East and West? Was it true that the Western society was freer than the Eastern? The answer must be yes in both cases, but there was not nearly as much meaning in the yes as was thought and held at the time. So much of Western democracy was sham; they kept the letter, but it was empty of spirit, as we see today on going over those ancient newspapers and magazines. Even if the foremost western freedom was the freedom to starve, as disgruntled democrats used to say at one period, the problem of personal freedom on the Eastern side was very real too. Freedom of choice and of movement, was incomparably higher in the West for a long time, unsatisfactory though this itself was for the non-rich multitudes. The new society was built with immense regimentation. Probably it could never have been built any other way in the first place. The Westerners always said it could; that more gradual development would have been much more successful. But it is interesting to note that Western capitalists never seemed to have done very much about developing the countries which afterwards "went Communist." Something was wrong; and it was not all on the Eastern side. The phrase "human freedom" has deep, fundamental meaning; the West ignored it too much, and the East much too much. Each side reaped the consequent results of this neglect in great subsequent difficulties.

In the course of history, the essentially practical argument between private enterprise and collectivist production worked itself out through a long series of compromises. It is not our task to enter into details of economics here. The social effects of the two systems, with their respective political machineries, are more to our point. There is no doubt that Western private enterprise, as we showed in our first chapter, finally became the gravest handicap to social progress; there was no alternative to its modification and transmutation. The Eastern Bloc's egging this process on avoided still greater waste of time. One could almost say that pace, rather than content, was of the essence in the matter, but not quite. When the Easterners forced the pace as they did, with brusqueness which reached terrible proportions in disrespect for human life (not that the Westerners, with their intolerably slowly cleared slums, had any too little of the latter), they did themselves and their cause immense damage, both politically and materially. The basic human material cannot be handled like that. The West went to the limits, and beyond them; the East went right beyond them without delay, and paid dearly in due course.

The main political problem for both sides was how to educate the people to a higher stage, since the people did not then know the necessary minimum for operating democracy. The Western leaders at their best hoped to do this without incurring the odium of dictatorship. The East worried less on this score at first, and did, as we have noted, give a great impetus to popular education, which influenced the West competitively. As education is a field in which competition between peoples is not harmful, we have no complaints here. But the political machinery of the East was not even as democratically contrived as its counterpart falsely was on the West. Both sides failed for a very long time. The educational problem in relation to politics from the democratic viewpoint was yet another instance of how the opposed approaches of East and West both failed for quite diverse reasons. It is all too easy to fail from different angles; and the utmost blowing of propagandist trumpets will not conceal the truth when historians have had enough time to get down to thorough research.

In the international field, the effects of the East-West dispute were so profoundly bad that mankind's progress was delayed wholesale that century and barely missed coming to an untimely end. We have no need to go into details: the story is well-known and a standard item in world history. Perhaps it had to come about, because the world was so terribly badly organized into incoherent "countries," descended from the very ancient tribal groups. It is impossible for us today to realize the primitive psychology still prevailing in the twentieth century. We are naturally appalled when we read the ancient tales of people lining up joyfully in myriads to slaughter other people, similar to them in all respects apart from minor cultural differences—giving their lives for their "countries" they called it. They had no little justification for slaughtering their politicians, but that they never thought of. There was a pacifist movement, it is true; but it had far too little mass appeal to develop influentially. The whole problem of war (and it really was a problem to the men of those times) was undoubtedly very much linked to the non-sanity of society in general.

The common man was ready and willing to participate in and perform the utmost horrors as long as they were in the name of his "country." This is a very fundamental expression of evolution, working through tribalism to preserve the type at all costs; but the dreadful thing about it was that it should continue into times of scientifically advanced civilization. The contradiction between man himself and his achievements is fearful to contemplate, as we look back over this ancient state of affairs. It is incredible to us that force was still used as the ultimate sanction, against all the dictates of reason and civilization itself. Yet brute force yet lay behind all government then. Proudhon, the great anarchist of the nineteenth century, had recognized and clearly stated this in his time, and matters were not one whit better a hundred years later.

Warlike action is impossible unless one regards the enemy as sub-human, fit only for destruction. This attitude was carefully fostered by the military authorities of the time. It was possible because of the deadly underlying loyalty to "country." Human morality was replaced by patriotism, not only easily, but with greatly increased intensification. The local group, the in-group, is a simpler basis for the elementary human psyche to work upon than the inclusive generality of the race. And a thousand years ago, no sort of moderately reasonable working agreement had been worked out among all humanity. Still today, and no doubt for immensely longer, loyalty may cut across balanced considerations of right and wrong. It is no light matter to throw over a friend or relative if he does wrong, for all that morality dictates. In those days loyalty to that wondrous personification, "country," became the curse of mankind.

The explanations for nationalism, typically of ever-increasing force during most of the twentieth century, are many and various. Aggression as an expression of self-preservation, exaggerated by fear of being stifled or simply outdone, allied to ancient tribalism (far from dead in the human mind) often producing utter caricatures of science in racism—these comprise a good explanatory group of reasons. It is hardly convincing to us, though. All this does not tell us why airmen set off calmly, time after time, to slaughter children and other human beings. They knew well enough what they were doing, but salved their consciences with no trouble, except in the rarest cases where neurosis was produced. They utilized many rationalizations of their actions: other airmen were probably doing the same to their children (revenge); it was in the name of greater good than evil, however regrettable (self-delusion); their officers gave the orders (this abandonment of self-responsibility was actually legally forbidden in the unusual small "country," Israel). They performed a mental trick quite common in ancient days: schizophrenically splitting the mind in two (at least), so that military "duty" had nothing to do with humanity, just as the most fantastic religious beliefs were successfully railed off, in the brain, from interfering with an excellent scientific outlook in other respects. Split mind was a frequent mental illness in those days; it was also very convenient for use when required on general occasions. It is only in comparatively recent times that such mental dishonesty has virtually died out in face of modern education and overall conscious unity of thought broadly achieved in upbringing. Of course we still have trouble with subconscious elements, but we are working on them energetically with our latest electrical techniques, and are beginning to register some successes already.

The best explanations as to why murder of individuals should be condemned, but mass-murder in war approved just because the magic word "war" cancelled all normal logic and morality, still leave us dissatisfied. H. J. Mackinder, in his *Democratic Ideals and Reality,* suggested yet another explanation of nationalism:

> What is it that in the last two or three generations has given much strength to the nationality movement? . . . Nationalist movements are based on the restlessness of intelligent young men who wish for scope to live the life of ideas and to be among those who 'can' because they are allowed to do. . . . Why were Athens and Florence the wonderful founts of civilisation which have made them the teachers of the world? They were small cities as we now count the size of cities, but they were sovereign cities both in the political and economic sense. . . . Think of the choice of activities open to the able young Florentine, to be practised, remember, in and for his native town, and with no need to go away to some distant capital. . . . If he were a painter, sculptor, or architect, he would be employed on the monuments of his own place instead of seeing them designed by some visiting great man. Of course, no one suggests that you should or could return to institutions on the Anthenian or Florentine scale, but the fact remains that you have drained your local life of most of its value and interest by the development of nation-wide class organization. . .

We can never know the psychology of the ancients sufficiently. Probably there was no one predominant cause for nationalism and war, but a concatenation of circumstances, as so often happens. Imperialism undoubtedly played a profound part. Fear was greatly enhanced by that very East-West ideological conflict, as the East gained power. Western politicians seemed to fear being overwhelmed or perhaps outdated at one period; the Eastern ones feared abolition at the hands of the West (with good reason for decades until they were strongly fortified). Even with all this, we are hard put to imagine how the common man could line up in millions, ready to murder on request. Probably the best explanations of all are that he secretly hoped he would be able to go through the performance without ever really having to hurt anybody, and that he was not strong enough to give up his own life, or at least a substantial part of his livelihood, as the price of disobeying his commanders and the politicians behind them. We do not ask people to be martyrs today; it is indeed asking too much, although there have been noble spirits who would rather give their own lives than take anyone else's, and so touch the peak of human morality.

At any rate, none of the ghastly tragedy would have been possible if there had not been that fatal organization of mankind into "countries," political entities run by politicians supported by economic interests, proudly giving expression to the most backward primitive characteristics of the people they ruled. We have all read stories of the face-saving diplomacy practiced in the ancient world, the childish standing on dignity, the whole nightmarish artificial set-up. We cannot help feeling thankful that we live at a later stage of history in which the unnecessary disaster of war cannot happen because there is not the political organization in existence which could operate it. They used to say in those days that war would go on in any and every circumstance; that if there were not nation-states and armaments, then people would start fighting again with sticks and stones. Of course, this excuse was quite ridiculous. Personal quarrels with sticks and stones have actually been known in our own time, it must be admitted, but they certainly had no bearing whatever on the subject of organized mass-war.

The whole matter was riddled with deceit from beginning to end. There was that peculiar deceit that in war, murder is not murder, but a glory and no crime; that death in war is the noblest of deaths, and not the most futile and disgraceful; that the greatness of a "country" depends on the accumulation of its armaments (that fantastic waste of resources, which held back the development of civilization overwhelmingly in that period). All this was presented almost irresistably to the deluded populations of those "countries." There can be no doubt that the politicians were adept at deceiving themselves, as well as everybody else. They seemed to think they were doing good by sanctioning and instigating the selling of exceedingly expensive arms in sundry corners of the world; they could not fully have realized the extraordinary moral evil of playing with people's lives in international politics, or they could not possibly have done it, have committed such crimes. We may say that people can lose their tempers on occasion, but we cannot today admit that civilized beings can ever be so crude as to desert all reasoning and resort to unintelligent force "en masse," using others as puppets. This is going far too far in the path of exasperation, to put matters mildly. "Civilization" was clearly not the right word to employ in regard to politicians of this brand.

It is impossible nowadays to understand the vile ferocity of such ancient figures as Mussolini, Franco, and Hitler, all belonging to the century in question. There were plenty more minor specimens, to say nothing of their innumerable henchmen. Even comparatively mild politicians, not actually Fascist barbarians, would have war continued, i.e. the killing maintained, during cease-fire talks; or an armistice would be arranged for a certain time and date, the mutual slaughter to be kept us as vigorously as possible until that exact hour. How cheap life was in that century! Such depths of degradation were but rarely reached in the earlier phases of man's history. And it all happened after so much advance had been made in many other fields. It only shows how fatally insecure the emotional, the psychological basis remained, until still deeper scientific advance could be made, at last awakening the moral conscience so that such horrors became impossible. The contemporary poet W. H. Auden has perhaps expressed something of the intellectual emotion experienced by those who actually witnessed the dreadful deeds concerned, but it is impossible for us to sense it now.

Try as we may, we can find little to bring forward in extenuation of this terrible sitatuion. There were rare instances when a local culture was threatened with extinction by jealous others and was justified in mobilizing all resources for defense and fighting back. There were those peculiarly half-hearted attempts at international political cooperation: the League of Nations and, after its total failure, its replacement, the ironically-named United Nations Organization. Truly enough, they were the beginnings of a better vision, inadequate as they were. But, mostly devoid of morality, as usual, they expressed little beyond power interests; considerations of right and wrong entered little into their political deliberations. Some good was done, but not nearly enough. We must put this down to the fact that a "country's" ruling politicians were regarded as the sacred purveyors of their nation's "spirit," whatever that was mythically imagined to be; not as bureaucratic individuals, which is all they were in reality. This was the external political myth, far more deadly than the internal one to which we have made previous reference. That primitive hallucinatory concept, "country," was always the culprit behind the scenes. "My country will never consent to..." or "My country demands full freedom of action in regard to..." were typical phrases used to begin speeches, blithely ignoring the fact that the opening phrase, "My country," was a verbal non-existent, and that there were only millions of people back home who would, with unimportant bigoted exceptions, have been only too pleased to consent to all kinds of things, for the sake of a little peace and quiet, and demanded no freedom of action whatever in regard to the other things, being perfectly content to leave them alone. False pride, pretence, deceit, lies—what a painful past to look back upon!

The moral failure of twentieth century civilization is nowhere more apparent than in the political field. The position was so bad that accepting it as historical fact (which it undoubtedly was) we put ourselves in the quandary of not being able to understand how progress was ever made to the quite reasonable state of affairs prevailing around our world today. Many of us feel intense allegiance to our regions, but not for a moment do we conflict with other people's allegiances and rights elsewhere. There will probably always be further experiments in democracy to work out, but at least we have achieved a sensible basis no longer questioned in essentials. Above all local difficulties and differences, we are primarily true citizens of the world. As a farseeing twentieth century commentator from the North American region, Stringfellow Barr, would have put it, "we have joined the human race." Yes, we have actually become real human beings by now, infinite through future development must be.

How was it done? It is a long story, a thousand-years-long story. In outline, everyone knows this story to some extent. It is sufficient to stress that most of the secret hinges on federation in all kinds of forms and applications. This was the basis of the progressive path, as readers will recollect if they think back over their more modern history for a moment. As the modern era dawned in earnest, the old split was healed, East and West finally met in the political field as in others. Only then did they together lay the foundations of the united world of our times, so brilliantly foreseen by Wells, its prophet, back in the badlands of history a millenium ago. Only then could the huge neglected and exploited areas of Earth and the unfortunate millions living in them be put in order, the new continents built, and colonization commenced on additional planets.

With this, we can take leave of the sorrowful aspects of the twentieth century and come to a happy ending after all, by turning our attention to one of the all too few bright spots of the ancient world, which so significantly laid some of the ideological and practical foundations of our own. It was a special spark of light in that mostly grim darkness, and it has never been forgotten. Our readers will recognize the subject by its name—a name which passed into history long ago and has remained there, continually renewed in practice, to this day.

# 6 Kibbutz!

Today, at the beginning of the thirtieth century, rather more than twenty per cent of the world's population lives in communes of a few hundred people each, distributed over every region in both town and country. They have never lost the name of kibbutz, which was given to this form of social living in ancient Israel, where it was first worked out on a comparatively large scale from the end of the year 1910 onwards. The name, taken from the Hebrew language there, means "group." The next area which took up the idea seriously was that of the East Asian Japanese islands (as they were then) basically as a means of agricultural development, although much more than merely this was added to it in both cases. The first Japanese kibbutz actually dated back to 1905, slightly earlier than the first Israeli one. But it was in Israel that this form of social organization first took on the form of a movement and thus became a fundamentally significant part of the unique little nation there. Development as a social movement duly took place in Japan too, and two-thirds of the way through the century, the movements got to know each other and the much more developed one in Israel was able to help its weaker partner to lay the foundations of its large-scale successes later on.

From much earlier times — at least the end of very ancient days, and possibly before — a few men had decided to live in community on occasion. No small importance attaches to this phenomenon, but very rarely did it have much social influence radiating from its nearly always religious basis. Until the Israeli and Japanese movements arrived on the scene and became of striking local significance one after the other on their opposite sides of Asia, only the so-called Hutterite Movement in North America (it had originally emigrated from Europe), already four centuries old, had reached appreciable size. Even so, it was a self-isolated, radically static affair, and by no means an integral part of the society of the region.

Outstanding importance, therefore, must be attributed to the Israeli kibbutz movement in the first place, and after to the Japanese and other movements around the world which developed in due course. The intense, pure, direct democracy of the kibbutz here, there, and everywhere, is an essential basis (probably *the* essential basis) for our modern world social organization. The concentrated human spirit of kibbutz members makes them just a little larger than life-size, as it were; they typically play a leading part over the whole range of communal human affairs. Of course, there are innumerable individual exceptions everywhere too; kibbutz members remain a small minority, varying somewhat from region to region, according to a local circumstances and customs, and in no way constitute a social elite. Nevertheless, the intensity of their communal life does make them the leaven of society in general to no small degree. It was the same in ancient Israel from the outset, where they led the national cultural revival of their people there and played a political and artistic part out of all proportion to their numbers. This is the effect of community living, and we have no difficulty in coming up with the appropriate scientific explanations now, although in those earliest days it was not effectively comprehended. It has always been recognized that only a minority of people are fitted for communal life; that specifically individualist characteristics are so predominant in about three quarters of humanity (as so far evolved) that insufficient cooperation-potential is available for increasing the kibbutz element in society to any great extent. However, as we gain additional scientific control over the human brain and personality, we hope to improve this situation. It is clear that there is nothing like kibbutz living for toning up the whole of society.

The actual history of the Israeli kibbutz movement can be found in the appropriate history books and does not concern us here. What does concern us is the underlying social drive behind the entire phenomenon of kibbutzism: where are its social roots? We need to know this in order to understand the significance of kibbutzim (it is interesting to note that we still use the ancient Hebrew masculine -im ending for this word in our world language today) in modern life, in addition to consideration of the fascinating historical aspects of the matter in man's social evolution. In order to approach the subject at all, we shall have to take up the theme of the Jewish people, who made such unique contributions to civilization, the kibbutz surely being the most outstanding of all in the practical field. It was so because of the particular characteristics of this people in general. So this is the first point to examine.

When making the striking, long quotation from an unidentifiable work of the twentieth century in our second chapter, that on science, we stated that it was taken from a book primarily devoted to Zionism, the special nationalist philosophy of the Jews. It is now especially convenient to return to that same book, and draw from its Zionist sections. We shall find them, too, illuminating. The unknown author makes out his case to show that early settlement on the Eastern Mediterranean coastlands, on the fringe of the desert, gave the Jews a radically different cultural start in life from other Bedouin Arabs in very ancient times. He says:

In reviewing subsequent history up to the twentieth century itself, he goes on to emphasize the continuity of the mental outlook of the Jewish people, long preserved in the religious life of the ghetto in many other people's lands when ancient imperialist wars turned this people out of its own. He goes on:

We do not think it is possible to exaggerate the importance of the facts that the Land of Israel is to be found at the cross-roads of three continents and, in those remote days, lay on the main route in the Fertile Crescent between the two major senior civilizations of Egypt and Sumer. Our tribe in search of pasture settled just at the place where cross-fertilization could ensure from the arousing thought of the two main civilizations of the entire Middle East.

The Jewish religion focuses the most intensive attention on ethics, and the ethical contribution of Judaism is generally regarded as of only moderately secondary importance to the religious one. The connection between the two is, in fact, so intimate that a statement exists (to our regret we have not been able to trace the origin) that 'Judaism has morality as its basis, and only through the practice of righteousness can we fulfil the Jewish life.' . . . Jewish ethics are those of a desert tribe in basis and are similar to those of any people brought up in hard or partially hard climatic conditions, where cooperation is the normal and essential attitude to life.

Extremely briefly, then, and with all the inadequacies consequent on extreme brevity, this is the underlying basis of it all.

Now abbreviating very much less, we proceed to the central subject itself:

How did the kibbutzim start? By mistake, we might almost answer. Certainly not on the basis of definite theory, although an admixture of various ones did enter into matters at least subconsciously. But they were really an organic growth of unique character, due to the unique conditions of the Land of Israel which those unique people, the Jews, wanted to recolonise and bring back to its former flourishing state as their unique program, Zionism, demanded. There was not at the outset any particular drive to reform society as such, although social idealism was not absent from the minds of the young people concerned at the beginning of the development. The aim was to resettle the land; by then a land declined through centuries of neglect into malarial swamp and barren hills. Private enterprise in the form of subsidised smallholding was failing to make good. The immigrating youngsters from Eastern Europe worked in the orange groves, the only thing that did pay, in difficult competition with Arab labour, strong and cheap. They built roads – anything to develop the land and maintain themselves. In hard conditions of living and climate, it was out of the question to lead lonely individualistic lives; it was essential, both physically and psychologically, to club together in order to survive at all and to conquer the land's difficulties and bring it back to fruitfulness of old. One of them, afterwards among the dozen founders of the first kibbutz, Degania, which was started in 1910 on the shores of the Jordan at the southern end of the Sea of Galilee, Miriam Baratz, explained the matter in these words: 'Our way of life was not based on a program or a theory. We wanted to live together, and we wanted to create something fine, and we called this a commune. Members worked for private farmers, each one receiving his monthly salary and depositing it with me, I disposing of it as I saw fit.' That is to say, she was the treasurer of the kibbutz. A collective household had been formed, the essence of the kibbutz in fact, and the foundations of the whole subsequent social structure was laid. Since a kibbutz is a unified economic household, private financial worries are eliminated; the family ceases to be a business and becomes a real family once more, undistorted by financial considerations and monetary competition; new vistas are opened up for individual lives to develop freely according to potentialities. Although fresh problems arise in turn, community living being no panacea for all the ills of society, the step forward is immense. Not a few of the primary barriers of competitive society to a satisfying and culturally progressive life are down; in many cases the individual can find himself in a kibbutz-type commune as he never could on his own. In old poetic terms one could describe it as losing one's soul in order to gain it. The financial problem remains, but it is collectivised; the impact on the individual is infinitely less. The kibbutz has to maintain itself by earning a profit, just as a private family must; but this process too is collectivised, and money-making no longer remains the prime personal concern.

The kibbutz made human life possible in a fuller sense than is generally feasible for any but those of assured financial status, and in some ways even more so than it can be lived by millionaires. For the democratic self-government necessarily implied by the kibbutz is denied to the autocrat; if the millionaire is no autocrat, he can hardly develop his social propensities by participating in communal living, unless he ignores social custom and pays his riches into the common fund of such a community, a gesture which has not yet been made. Digging a little deeper, we see that the kibbutz is founded on that basic equality which gives every individual his full human dignity; the connection with Jewish social ethics is obvious. There is nothing merely theoretical about kibbutz equality between members. Perhaps its overwhelming social significance lies in its eradication of the two classes of humanity, masters and servants. All members contribute their share to the dirty work of their village: the household services. Only a few small religious communities have perhaps ever achieved this final and complete solution of the class problem. The kibbutz has done it, not on a religious basis but on an ethical one. Here we have a truly equalitarian society; as a result, the social conscience is developed to the utmost and the member has a full chance of achieving human stature in something like the highest degree.

We have no need to remind our readers of what we said in our first chapter about the evils of money in twentieth century society, and connected matters of social morality. Here we see that even in those generally deplorable times the Jewish people had already found the answer, as though by accident. Speaking for ourselves, we do not see it as altogether an accident. It seems a logical outcome of Jewish social ethics. Our author does make a somewhat minimal reference in this respect, but subsequent research lays rather more stress on those ethics. The matter is a subtle one, and out of the question to investigate here.

We now need to review the general description of the kibbutz of that ancient time, in order to relate communal living to social living. A whole millenium afterwards, there are no really fundamental changes. It is true that owing to vastly more advanced sience and technology, the modern kibbutz looks and is not a little different from the ancient sort. The ancient kind was based on farms, although there was also industry; Of course, there is no such primitive a phenomenon as that any more. All this, though, is not very important. Communal life is community life in any age. The entire orientation and outlook is different and infinitely more social. Even in our own times, the well-socialized individual is not so socially advanced in character as the kibbutz member. In those days, naturally, the difference was far greater still. They had difficulty in maintaining the kibbutz percentage of the population at even five per cent and could not dream of twenty. Besides, there were no kibbutzim at all in towns, where the competitive social atmosphere was hopelessly loaded against them. It took them a very long time to conquer this difficulty. No matter; as we said, the essentials were all there. We can still use the ancient kibbutz as a pattern, although some of its details are bound to sound rather quaint nowadays.

In its very earliest days, a kibbutz could carry on with scarcely any organization at all. The entire membership — only a handful in any case — would meet every evening after work at the outset to discuss affairs, make necessary arrangements, and leave it at that. Later on, when more and more members were taken in by communal consent, and when the affairs of the commune became more complex, it was necessary to have not only a treasurer and secretary, but a farm manager, someone to make purchases in town, someone to be in charge of education, and so on. Almost imperceptibly, but quite quickly, a fairly complete form of social organization was built up; an organic democratic growth set in of necessity. Persons were agreed upon as heads of agricultural branches, others of household services. To the main functionaries were added committees, reasonably termed the life-blood of democracy, so that members could in turn cooperate in and learn the inner details of all the affairs of the kibbutz. The central committee, or secretariat, became the general executive authority and the coordinating one between the rest of the committees, a sort of day-to-day government, itself responsible, like the other functionaries and committees, to the general meeting, the kibbutz as a whole. One can make an obvious comparison with standard parliamentary democracy, but the comparison is not nearly exact, for the kibbutz is a unity and the members of its government are in no way a separate, outside body, even temporarily during the period of officeholding. They are at all times simple members of the kibbutz as well. Moreover, the concept of "parties" is impossible within the kibbutz framework, for political parties are the expression of conflicting groups among a heterogeneous population, while the kibbutz is united in its interest of building a profitable village and a satisfying communal life for its members on a basis of the utmost equality. Conflicting political parties serving different interests cannot possibly exist; only one united "party" is possible, and the whole kibbutz is that.

Most interesting, as our readers will agree, after what we wrote ourselves in our political chapter on parties and the one-party system! In ancient days understanding people who grasped the basic essentials of human social organization also knew what they were talking about. We find exactly the same thing even if we turn back to very ancient times. The very ancient Greeks have left us writings of the utmost penetration and subtlety on political themes in particular (although by no means on these alone.) Similarly, the very ancient Jews, still earlier, some four thousand years ago, bequeathed noble writings on morality to us and all men at all periods. The fundamentals of human conduct remain unchanged in all ages. Thus men can talk to each other in books across the centuries. We continue to quote:

> When a kibbutz becomes really large, comprising some hundreds of members, the purely technical side of its organisation then amounts to something quite formidable. It is not only a

large business, probably industrial as well as agricultrual; it is also a sizeable village, needing full local government services. The members must be at one and the same time business partners and village councillors, working and administrating, organising and carrying out life in all its aspects, while developing their personal and family interests. To the outsider, the task may seem to be too much, the matter unwieldy and impracticable. The kibbutz proves its strength in all its sectors by shouldering its burdens with outstanding success. This is not to say there is not grave strain on the members in some cases, most especially in medium and small young kibbutzim suffering from shortage of manpower to operate an economy of minimum effective size. But unity is strength no less in the kibbutz than elsewhere, and inter-kibbutz help in the worst cases at the worst times is invaluable.

Generally speaking, members are appointed to posts for one year only, but there are some posts which demand so much specialist knowledge that it has been found impracticable to train people, get them used to the responsible work involved, and then withdraw them a short while after. For such posts two or three years are allowed before a changeover is demanded. Heads of industrial or farm branches may be allowed much longer still; but it is generally agreed that even when a post is primarily technical and not administrative, elements of control over other members (although co-workers) do enter in, and a definite limitation to term of office is desirable. The frequent changeover of functionaries is the best safeguard agains bureaucracy. However, it is not absolutely foolproof in the kibbutz, for if the changes are rung on a limited circle of members with clear organising and other ability, allowing them a year or two's rest and then reelecting them, the problem of democratic leadership is by no means solved. Democracy, however pure, does demand leadership, but of a special kind. This democratic leadership is of a moral nature and can be given almost imperceptibly. It is really a setting of the social tone by those possessed of the profounder human qualities It can readily be expressed almost continuously in the kibbutz general meeting, the perfect forum for mutual education. The true moral leaders of a kibbutz do not need to be constant office-holders; they can, from time to time, be comparatively minor committee members and still make their influence felt through others to the general good. . . .

The mental orientation of the kibbutz member is quite distinct from that of an ordinary villager who pays but limited attention to village affairs as a whole. If everyone knows everybody else in every village, in a kibbutz everyone knows everybody else very much better, or, of course, worse! For the members eat together, plan together, play together, as well as work together in groups. A member's life is not delimited by his personal interests and those of his family alone, although they naturally have full expression; he thinks and lives in a wider framework, a family of families; his outlook inevitably broadens to encompass the community; his loyalty is to his kibbutz, as well as to his own family and friends within the kibbutz. As a result, he is a larger man in the human sense. He learns to see the problems of his local society and consequently of all human society. He becomes sufficiently broad-minded and tolerant to cooperate in matters and with people a purely private person would rarely, if ever, contemplate.

Apart from pocket money for small personal items (mostly bus fares, books and small presents for children and others), money is totally unknown in the kibbutz from the internal angle. Members travelling on official kibbutz business naturally have their expenses paid, and those few kibbutz members who work outside in specialist capacities ranging from bus driver to Member of Parliament or technical teacher, United Nations expert or assistant in a governmental planning department, pay their earnings into the common fund when they come home, again after deducting expenses.

Here we would draw attention to the undoubted fact that life takes on quite a different coloring when money is not involved. Instead of measuring most things almost automatically in terms of currency, as outside people can hardly avoid doing ("What does it cost? - Is it worth it?"), the kibbutz member takes things for what they are. His standard is use-value, not exchange-value. Of the two, the former is undoubtedly the more realistic; things are for use, not for everlasting exchange. Owing to human psychology, money persistently penetrates far beyond its place to interfere with all manner of human activities and their valuations in a field where it has no place whatever — that of human worth. The moneyless kibbutz gives human values their full chance of expression. A man is judged for what he is, not for what he has, and ethical development has every chance of going ahead without undue distortion from the outset. Collectively, but only collectively, the kibbutz discusses investments, profits and losses on the grand scale like any business magnate, but this is rather theoretical in atmosphere and somewhat far removed mentally from the daily life of the kibbutz member, in spite of its being severely practical in determining the member's standard of living. The mere fact that monetary affairs have been set at a little distance by being made collective instead of individual, has taken the social poison out of them and rendered them innocuous.

Our readers will agree that applause is appropriate at this point. Our unknown author undoubtedly knew what he was talking about. It is quite possible that he was a kibbutz member himself, and this would account for his outlook being already far ahead of his time in general, regarding social affairs. He had already reached something comparable with our own and any modern view on healthy and unhealthy social life. This alone speaks volumes for the value of the kibbutz to an individual, if he was indeed a member. If not he was an observant social analyst, to say the least. True, he was not the only one by far, as our varied and various quotations prove. But the fact remains that any such criticism was rare in the extreme. We selected our quotations with the greatest care, and can assure our readers that we had to inspect nearly a ton of twentieth century publications before we could find material of this level of penetration. So rarely could the veil of smug acceptance be completely lifted that there were very few cases in that century when really basic social principles were tackled fearlessly. Comparatively mild, and occasionally harder, criticism was common enough, as we stated in Chapter 1, but even that was never acted upon to any extent. Questioning of commonly accepted fundamentals, such as the free use of money by the individual (if he had any worth talking about) in total disregard of general need was indeed rare. Such things were not queried because society was too rigid in its uneasy weakness. It was, in every respect, too dangerous to go so far. If, as on those rarest occasions, anyone did, they could regard the matter only as a fantasy, thus ruling it out of court and rendering it harmless. We know, from certain newspaper and magazine articles, that the Israeli kibbutz, to say nothing of the Japanese one, was not infrequently regarded very much askance. Quite obviously it challenged the everyday world and could be seen as constituting a grave threat. That is, it would have been so seen if large numbers of people had flocked to the kibbutzim. But since the life always demanded extra cooperativeness, total kibbutz population until the end of the century was relatively small, and the threat was no more than theoretical. However, it annoyed some people, who sensed what was involved. How those twentieth century folk would be shocked to see world society today, well besprinkled with kibbutzim by way of essential examples of advanced cooperation, and generally beyond considerations of money except for special accounting purposes, plenty for all having been achieved at last! Now all but the rarest items can be distributed universally according to need and fancy, as only air was a thousand years ago (not even water, which had to be paid for!). We have all reached the kibbutz stage in this respect at any rate.

But to return to that interesting and so advanced book for the last time:

> It can be regarded as quite certain that there are no other villages in the world comparable with the Israeli kibbutzim for richness of cultural life in all its aspects. So much so that not only villagers but probably most town-dwellers do not enjoy anything like such good facilities (apart from upper-middle and upper-class ones who have everything at their disposal). The towns themselves are, after all, open to kibbutz members; but, in addition, they gain such benefits from their own communal organization and from the educational and artistic resources in the hands of the kibbutz federation to which they belong, that there is no possibility for them to lead a virtually non-cultural life as is all too common in towns and other villages themselves. Communal living unavoidably involves mutual education. Those with greater resources within themselves than the average naturally tend to pass on their knowledge to others, in general discussion, in committees, in study groups and artistic circles, and so guide the public opinion of the membership to favor increased cultural activity. The advantages of communal living are such, having regard also to the great economy of time afforded by communal housekeeping, that the national culture today is perhaps better found in the kibbutzim than anywhere else in the country.

We should naturally have liked to bring details from the Japanese and other kibbutzim also, but lack of space prevents us from making more than one essential remark about the former. There were a number of local-custom differences between the Japanese kibbutzim and the Israeli ones, but the outstanding difference was that the former deliberately exercised members' capacity to interact emotionally on the basis of intellectual persuasion in frequent special meetings devoted to this purpose. This practice was not uniform or universal, but it was widespread and generally accepted. It had some relation to the Zen Buddhism of the ancient East, but we should interpret it more scientifically as an intentional exercise of interradiating personality auras. It is an excellent instance of the actual East — mankind's original Eastern civilization, that is — having been able to make an intuitive approach to the matter of personality radiation long before the comparatively crudely materialistic Westerners got there scientifically. Mostly Jews — Israelis regathered together from all over their world dispersion — acted as a very important bridge between East and West in all matters in the end (the East and West political Blocs, as well as geographically Eastern and Western cultures), but they organized their national life in the Western manner, and therefore their kibbutzim did not include this "Kensan," as it was named, and allied Japanese communitarian practices. It was a pity they did not, for doing so could have welded their memberships still more closely together, perhaps improving their achievements even more. Nowadays we can handle matters more effectively by scientific methods, but we can yet regard the ancient Japanese kibbutz "Kensan" practices with approval.

The reader will remember that very near the beginning of this book, we quoted a basic excerpt from Erich Fromm's very notable work, *The Sane Society.* It is extremely appropriate at this point to return to this book and so to link matters back to our beginning.

. . . True decisions cannot be made in an atmosphere of mass voting, but only in the relatively small groups corresponding perhaps to the old Town Meeting and comprising not more than let us say five hundred people. In such small groups the issues at stake can be discussed thoroughly, each member can express his ideas, can listen to, and discuss reasonably other arguments. People have personal contact with each other, which makes it more difficult for demagogic and irrational influences to work on their minds. . .

We do not need new ideals or new spiritual goals. The great teachers of the human race have postulated the norms for sane living. Today, it is not Baal and Astarte but the deification of the

State and of power in authoritarian countries and the deification
of the machine and of success in our own culture; it is the
all-pervading alienation which threatens the spiritual qualities of
man...

Religious rituals have little importance any more, except for
the Catholics. Secular rituals hardly exist. Aside from the
attempts to imitate rituals in lodges, fraternities, etc., we have a
few patriotic and sport rituals, appealing only to a most limited
extent to the needs of the total personality. We are a culture of
consumers. We "drink in" the movies, the crime reports, the
liquor, the fun. There is no active productive participation, no
common unifying experience, no meaningful action-out of
significant answers to life. What do we expect from our young
generation? What are they to do when they have no opportunity
for meaningful, shared artistic activities? What else are they to do
but to escape into drinking, movie-daydreaming, crime, neurosis
and insanity? What help is it to have almost no illiteracy and the
most widespread higher education which has existed at any
time – if we have no collective expression of our total
personalities, no common art and ritual? Undoubtedly a relatively
primitive village in which there are still real feasts, common
artistic shared expressions, and no literacy at all – is more
advanced culturally and more healthy mentally than our
educated, newspaper-reading, radio-listening culture.

No sane society can be built upon the mixture of purely
intellectual knowledge and almost complete absence of shared
artistic experience, college plus football, crime stories plus Fourth
of July celebrations, with Mothers' and Fathers' Day and
Christmas thrown in for good measure. In considering how we
can build a sane society, we must recognize that the need for the
creation of collective art and ritual on a nonclerical basis is at
least as important as literacy and higher education. The transformation of an atomistic into a communitarian society depends
on creating again the opportunity for people to sing together,
walk together, dance together, admire together – together, and
not, to use Riesman's succinct expression, as a member of a
"lonely crowd."

It might be an advertisement for the kibbutz! Not that the kibbutz
was in any way an illiterate, primitive village; precisely the reverse. It

was the outside world then which was less than primitive, culturally speaking, as Fromm said. His emphasis on togetherness was the cardinal point: the kibbutzim never ceased to echo this emphasis. The best simple and direct explanation of the Israeli kibbutz written at that time (which we have been able to discover) was, in fact, most aptly called *Together.* Originally a Hebrew textbook for kibbutz youth, admirably taught thus in the fundamentals of their way of life by a founder-member named Mordechai Amitai, this has been preserved for us only in translations into other ancient languages. It seems that it was intended also for converting some of the outside youth left stranded in the deplorable condition Fromm described. We must surely hope it succeeded at least a little in its purpose, but knowing the inordinate strength of the established order in the twentieth century (based on hardly anything more solidly constructive than social inertia, the political myths, and all the rest of the sad story we have sought to review in this book) we must be permitted to retain our doubts.

It is particularly interesting to note that Fromm, although outstanding, was by no means the only voice then calling for an appreciably kibbutzised society, without, apparently, in the least realizing that a remarkable specimen was lying at their hand in Israel already. That same Mackinder, whom we quoted before in connection with external politics (nationality), also writes thus:

> (The Londoner) lives in a suburb; he is shot through a tube to an office-room in the City, and then shot back to his bedroom in the suburb; only on Saturdays and Sundays has he time for communal life, and then he amuses himself with neighbours who are tied to him by nothing essential. In the great majority of cases he never comes into living contact with a large and trained mind except through the printed page: for him, as for the industrial worker in the country, his life of ideas is detached from his responsible life, and both suffer infinitely in consequence . . . By proper control, you could have substituted a 'village region' with a community dependent on each factory or group of small factories, wherein rich and poor, masters and men, might have been held together in a neighbourly responsible relationship; but you have allowed instead the East and West Ends to grow up in your great cities . . . the slums, and most other material afflictions of the people are the outcome of impotence of local life, for they

all result from offences against the principle of keeping that life complete and balanced. Provinces of complete life, of course, imply a federal system . . . Athens and Florence were great because they saw life whole . . . In the growth of brains and contentment something far more subtle is involved than any technical education or healthy housing. Is it quite certain that at the end of a century of refusal to get rich as quickly as possible, we should not have been far richer than we are? . . .

With too many of us, in our urban and suburban civilization, that grand old word Neighbour has fallen almost into desuetude. It is for Neighbourliness that the world today calls aloud, and for a refusal to gad ever about — merely because of modern opportunities for communication . . . Neighbourliness or fraternal duty to those who are our fellow-dwellers, is the only sure foundation of a happy citizenship. Its consequences extend upward from the city through the province to the nation and to the world league of nations. It is the cure alike of the slumdom of the poor and of the boredom of the rich, and of war between classes and war between nations.

While, as we see, the social analysis in this book *Democratic Ideals and Reality,* does not go sufficiently deep, the essence is there. Neighborliness, after all, is a synonym for togetherness.

Let us look at a statement by a contemporary journalist, Dorothy Thompson, virtually advertising the kibbutz as a small-scale edition of her ideal society, in "I Believe: Ten Articles of Faith":

All creative functions in society are of equal value. The mechanic is not inferior to the scholar, nor the scholar to the mechanic, nor the farmer to the industrial worker, nor the worker to the planner or executive. Compensation for various activities should not vary so greatly that vastly differing social classes are created. A social order should be sought which is not the stratified order of masters and slaves, or management and workers, nor a categorized order of exclusive casts of administrators, intellectuals, farmers and industrial workers, but is integrated as an orchestra is integrated, in which the piccolo player is recognized as no less essential than the violinist, and the unity of the whole, from the conductor down, is imposed by the music scheduled to be played. The score of the social music is the common purpose of the people.

Or let us turn to a very different journalist, Kingsley Martin, who, in a book called *The Press the Public Wants,* wrote:

> First let me say that I do not believe that it is either possible or desirable to turn all men into "cosmopolitans" — that is to say, into Citizens of the World without roots in smaller democratic communities. Rousseau . . . held the right end of the stick when he urged that democracy was possible only in a small community, and that freedom could not be achieved in a large state unless it was divided into districts and given a federal constitution. . . The solution, I suggest, lies in increasing decentralization of administration and the revivifying of community life. This is only possible if the smaller region is part of a far wider federal whole. . . Let me assume a world that is not yet in sight — a world in which sovereignty has been abolished, an International Council maintaining the peace, and a federal organization determining the structure of our economic life. In that case we should be able to return to our proper political and social interest, which is in the small area round ourselves. Real democracy would then be possible.

As we well know it is today. Mr. Martin, incidentally, knew his Wells. But there were still more compatriots of that greatest Briton of them all, like Mr. Mackinder, who were not so much intrigued necessarily by problems of world organization. One such was a certain John Macmurray, whose Scottish name-prefix reminds us that the very few people, the Scots or North Britons, who lived at the far end of the main British island, composed a veritable salt of the earth in their way in their time, for they were possessed of the most unusually penetrating intellects. How far the Scottishness of this particular Macmurray went, we have not been able to trace (innumerable minor, intimate items must inevitably get lost in far less than a thousand years) but the penetrating intellect was indubitably there in any case. The title of the book of his from which we now reproduce an excerpt (it is taken from the very end) was certainly enough to frighten fatally almost any Westerner of his period: *The Philosophy of Communism* of all things! It must have been published for excessively small circles in the West indeed. At any rate, not much harm could have been done, for it seems that it dealt for the most part with the very opposite of the official brand of Communism. At the beginning of our extract, it will be seen that the author cavalierly throws economic determinism to the winds, which, of course, is enough to make a twentieth century standard Communist reach for his pistol without delay. But as will be seen at the end of the extract, what the author is really getting at is not that standard political Communism in the least, but kibbutzic communitarianism, which is something like its opposite. And it is its opposite in this context because of its voluntary, local self-government (pure, direct democracy, we stress once more), which seems to have stemmed, in some measure from the anarchist element in human nature. It would be out of place here to take up the matter of the intellectual conflict in the nineteenth century between Marx and Proudhon (which makes very interesting reading, by the way). But we can state that we have never been able to trace any treatment of the twentieth century kibbutz from the anarchist standpoint, which is odd. We feel sure some such comparative research must have been made, in view of the quite obvious though indirect connection. We refer, obviously, to the intense individualism which lies behind anarchism as a social theory, and the willingness to produce a workable social system from it by local and syndicalist organization (the latter reminding us of the kibbutz federations the Israelis always formed for nation-wide economic, technical, cultural, and political purposes). In passing, we might mention that we feel, from our great distance in time, that the ideological conflict between the Western and Eastern Blocs may have had a great deal to do with the Communist-Anarchist intellectual gulf of outlook. We are aware, naturally, that a Westerner of that time would not appreciate being called an anarchist; nor, in fact, are we attempting to call him anything really like that. We merely suggest a loose connection between theoretical individualist anarchism and his own brand of individualism. As to the latter, we are bound to feel, looking backwards, that it defeated itself in the end, exactly as foretold in the excerpt we must now give, considering the self-alienation and social alienation it gave rise to:

> The creation of a classless society through the destruction of economic privilege is . . . the immediate, rational end of our social development. But its rationality and its necessity are not derived from any economic determinism. They are grounded in the essential nature of human personality, of which economic need is only one aspect, however important. What is required as the basis of any communist society is that we should escape from

individualism in our personal life. It is quite possible to secure economic equality for a society of confirmed individualists. It might, indeed, be forced upon them by the instinct for self-preservation. But such a society would necessarily be based, like Hobbes' Leviathan, on sheer force. It would involve a permanent dictatorship over the whole field of national life. From any human point of view it would be a "reductio ad absurdum" of individualism. The last effort to preserve one's precious self would have consisted in the destruction of everything that gives selfhood a positive significance.

Communism is not ultimately a matter of economics, even though it carries as a consequence some approach to economic equality. It is a matter of the inherently social nature of human personality. It must rest upon the need that men and women feel for living their lives in community. This, indeed, is the real need of all human nature. Against its achievement there stands the long tradition of the struggle to achieve free individuality, and the fear in men and women who are still unsure of themselves that their individuality would be swamped in any form of communal existence. It is this fear which is the secret motive in all the forms of opposition to the socialization of life. The answer to it is simple. That fear must inevitably produce the very fate that it dreads. 'He that saveth his life shall lose it.' Individuality can only maintain itself in community. Hitherto the development of individualism has been possible only through the family, and therefore, because women have been prepared to waive their claims to be free individuals. But now in increasing numbers they are insisting on their rights to express and maintain their individual independence. That claim cannot and should not be denied. But we must recognise that an individualism which embraces all individuals irrespective of sex means the disintegration of society into its constituent atoms. Long before that point is reached, it will become necessary for the State to enforce some form of organized social cooperation to take the place of the natural sociality which is being lost. Beyond a certain point the development of individualism means the destruction of individuality. There is only one way in which we can escape from some form of State-communism maintained by a dictatorship of force, which would destroy freedom and with it individuality, and that is by creating a form of community life which is

compatible with the individuality of all its members. In either
case the economic class-structure of capitalist society has to go.
Individualism and communism are opposites and irreconcilable.
Individuality and community are correlatives.

A mostly grand finale to a book, and one of the best-ever pleas for
practical kibbutzism in all society. What an immeasurable distance from
the original Bolshevik Communism, as they called it, to the applied
humanism of the kibbutz community, for which our last author so
vigorously pleaded! Such was the fatal muddle into which twentieth
century civilization had got itself through its lack of moral values to
any serious degree. (No little of that muddle was obviously semantic.
Men deceived themselves by words in that period as well as by many
other means). Just a handful of them could see clearly and farther. One
such was a renownedly serious sociologist named Karl Mannheim. He
quite frankly stated that the masses were so acted upon by mass
communication channels that they could easily run amok, being both
ignorant and frightened. Realizing that an unprincipled power elite held
social responsibility, the masses arrived at cynical despair. He concluded
his comment to the effect that instead of men being real personalities in
face-to-face groups, they became mere cyphers in the huge conurba-
tions of the time. This amounts to a most concise statement of the
position, again fully forcible, and in effect ending with yet another plea
for the kibbutz!

Somewhat amusing, by way of contrast, was the oddly grudging
praise given to the Israeli kibbutz itself by a brilliant contemporary
journalist-author, Arthur Koestler. He had lived in various kibbutzim
over extended periods, having lived in Palestine (the old name for the
land which became the State of Israel) and Israel at various times for
more than three years during the relevant transition period. One of his
novels was based on what he fondly imagined was kibbutz psychology
in the early days of the movement. According to the criticism
unearthed in connection with this book of his, *Thieves in the Night*, he
was remarkably far off the mark. At any rate, he did manage to get as
far as saying what follows:

> The absence of privileges for the bureaucracy prevented its
> crystallisation; they had no army, police or party apparatus to
> support them, their actions down to the minutest detail were
> under constant public scrutiny, and the principle of total

economic equality, outlawing money and barter, made it impossible for them to bestow favors or bribe the electorate. Their only satisfactions were increased responsibility, a more direct influence on the development of the commune, and the sensation of power derived from it. It was but the shadow of power, without substance and stability, and yet for those who wielded it real enough to be cherished more than they were prepared to admit, even to themselves. The instinct to dominate had not been abolished, merely tamed and harnessed; but that . . . was as much as anybody could hope for.

Of course, the model society of the commune was limited both in size and by the necessary selection of its human material. Repeated on a large scale and by compulsory means it was bound to collapse. Oases are not expandable. But it had been proved that under certain conditions a different form of human life could be attained; and that again was as much as one could hope for. . .

Entirely lacking here is the real vision of a generally finer society to come. And we cannot say that all is well as far as it goes. We have examined the contemporary evidence in documents as much as anyone can by now, and we are very doubtful that Koestler was right about kibbutz members of that age drawing satisfaction from the sensation of power when holding office for a year or two in some post or committee. We are not even at all sure that increased responsibility gave them any satisfaction. All the still available written and printed evidence indicates that they did not like it at all and that it caused them much worry, which they tried to escape as far as possible (perhaps a worse failing). No one can be sure nowadays. It is possible that something remaining from the power complexes of the outside world did remain in the kibbutzim then. After all, they had not even reached the stage of extracting raw aggression from children's brains by a very small electrical operation, as we regard as essential for safety's sake nowadays.

But this particular piece of writing about the kibbutzim seems to us oddly baffling in view of Koestler's other published work, which was extraordinarily modern in outlook for his time, from our point of view. This is especially true of his later work, for he had grasped the vital fact of the grossly uneven development of the sections of the human brain, which had resulted in considerable intellectual prowess being accompanied by almost entirely crude, primitive emotionalism. Apart from this, though, he had realized much of the essence of the human dilemma even in his comparatively early, brilliant book of essays, *The Yogi and the Commissar*. At the very end of this book, he pointed to the difficulty of the individual retaining his wholeness and yet operating as a mere part of society. Wellsian appeals to the intellect, he said, would never lead to the requisite integration of personality. (He apparently ignored the often very highly-charged emotional writing of Wells, with its almost poetically phrased inspirational qualities, such as we quoted in our relevant chapter.) Instead, he demanded practical living experience; personal integrity, but unity in one's society. Surely the kibbutz was exactly the place to attain this desirable one-ness in all-ness, personal life in a unified community. No such thing could be imposed from above; it had to be voluntary, and voluntary the kibbutz always was. For sufficiently broadminded people, it was the ideal way out. Though these were in the minority, their example and influence for good could and did count for much. So we cannot understand to-day why Mr. Koestler was as unfavorably critical of the kibbutz as he was, instead of welcoming it, with all its undoubted imperfections and human failings, as an ally on his side.

Moreover, in this same book of essays, analyzing the inhumanity of the Soviet Russian system, he listed the original Bolshevik incentives as including collectivism instead of competition; communal responsibility and voluntary discipline; equalitarian fraternity, a recognition of the dignity of labor and so on. Communist practice was, of course, the reverse of any such ideals. But the Israeli kibbutz just got down to the job and carried it out. Why our author did not recognize the achievement publicly and gratefully, in spite of its small scale, remains a mystery. In later times the scale, although not dominant, became very large—a possibility he never considered. He seemed to regard the kibbutz as essentially a curiosity, unsuitable for wide extension; while he praised it as achieving remarkable things in social organization, the grumble about personal power was put in to offset even this. We emphasize this to indicate that even in a case without any enthusiastic linkup of the kibbutz and man's pressing social needs, the kibbutz did make its impression; the praise was given, such as it was.

The view that the kibbutz demonstrated a finer way of life "under certain conditions," which was "as much as one could hope for" was undoubtedly general enough. To many people of the age it was a form of social organization applicable only in special circumstances, such as idealistically reclaiming a very ancient, lost homeland (Zionism), or putting very poverty-stricken agricultural living on its feet (the Japanese example). We admit there was some force in this view in those early times. All too few men were then naturally cooperative to even the moderate extent minimally necessary in a kibbutz. One early Israeli town-kibbutz experiment (of which records have been preserved) did fail due to this very lack of cooperation. Yet, as the spread of the kibbutz in later centuries proves, the application of the kibbutz to human society in general was immensely greater than almost anyone could have imagined back then. Mankind needed the kibbutz badly, not only for agricultural revivification (although the kibbutz, on account of its equalitarian, cooperative working, was the ideal instrument for this), but for all the socio-moral reasons which are by now undoubtedly quite clear in our readers' minds.

Yet there were actually kibbutz members, after something like half a century of kibbutz operation, who claimed that the kibbutz was not for export from Israel. We can read this in their movement magazine articles. The fact is that they did not know what a good thing they were on to from a universalist point of view, although they were aware of its advantages and could analyze them with great sociological prowess. The kibbutz, from the outset, was far more important than those who lived in it ever realized. It is on record that this was even actually said, in the local setting, and after half a century's experience, by Miriam Baratz of Degania, the first Israeli kibbutz of all, whom we quoted before. "We had no idea we were setting on foot such a wonderful enterprise as later spread over the length and breadth of the land," she said (or words to that effect, for the ancient diary is only uncertainly decipherable now). "As later spread over the length and breadth of the entire world," she could have said if only she could have lived for a millenium! But she learned the truth of the matter only in its limited Israeli setting. She and her fellow-founders had hit on the basic principles of social organization by the simple process of living in community and building it up naturally and organically, and this without understanding at the time what they were doing in the underlying sense. And since it was the right thing in the right place and time, it could not but develop, with unlimited possibilities for future expansion.

At the same time, we must not exaggerate, but must set the matter out fairly, once more. Not only was the Israeli kibbutz movement beaten by five years by the beginning of the Japanese movement, but there were communes of various shapes and sizes in earlier centuries too, although they rarely coalesced into movements. The development in the Japanese islands was very slow in this respect, and cannot be compared with the remarkable facility with which the Israeli kibbutzim rapidly federated into political groups, suited to the local circumstances of the time, and set up in and from themselves extensive specialist departments enriching every aspect of their members' lives. Moreover, the fact of a stray experimental Japanese kibbutz existing just before the first Israeli one is a chronological trifle of no real significance. Development in the kibbutz field in Eastern Asia was most scanty, scattered and incoherent for many decades. Only at the beginning of the second half of the century did it take on serious (although still very small) proportions, thanks to a few outstanding leaders. Only two-thirds of the way through the century did the Japanese news reach Israel itself, due to apparently chance contacts between one or two Japanese professors and one or two North American ones also well versed in this kind of sociology, along with increasing Japanese visits to Israel for practical observation. Still later did it become generally known. So, while we do make the necessary acknowledgements elsewhere around the world, the kibbutz movement in Israel must be recognized as holding far and away the most important place in kibbutz history: the source, in the course of its rapid organic growth, of most of the fundamentals of kibbutzism in theory and practice. The only serious exception is the "Kensan" of the Japanese movement, mentioned above. Later on, a few other items, originally similarly local in spirit, came in to the growing stream as it began to encircle the globe, but the basis was already fully laid. The key point to an understanding of this basis is the fact that the Israeli movement was a natural and essential translation into practice of the Zionist idealism of the Jewish people. This, in turn, was the logical outcome of their religion which, as we saw, was remarkably ethical in character. Kibbutzism, therefore, was a natural product of this unique people, who made of it an invaluable gift to the rest of humanity, for it was they who first turned it into a successful large-scale living-enterprise.

The kibbutz brought a new dimension to practical social ethics. If one definition of history is the story of man's striving for the perfect form of government, we have in the kibbutz, federated into the rest of society, at least an intermediate consummation of history. Whatever the future may bring (and experiments will always go on while man is in occupation of this and other planets) every society will necessarily utilize the kibbutz, the basic autonomous local unit, as the warp (whatever other elements may form the weft) of the social fabric. For it is in the kibbutz that politics come true; that ordinary people make and live them. And so a frame for the social art is assured. Even in ancient Israel itself, one or two rare writings preserved show that a few people did realize that the kibbutz constituted a socio-moral elite; almost the only sort of elite, by definition, which can do no harm, but only leadership-good to society. In a word, it was the social conscience of the people, and it still is. It can be nothing other. For kibbutz-members are bound to attend to their social as well as their individual affairs, or their community would collapse. Mutual aid is thus a "sine qua non"; man at last becomes fully human, because he is placed in a social setting where he has no alternative. Even in this, we naturally speak in general terms. We have heard of rare, but grave, backslidings. Human beings are not, as yet, put into the world fully guaranteed. The kibbutz has no patent for producing angels. All it can promise is that it will not produce robots and that to no small extent it will definitely produce some human beings a grade or two finer than usual. This is a moderate and partial guarantee, but it is sufficient. It is what gives the kibbutz its justification as the leaven in society.

There is so much the kibbutz gives to man in his social framework. Its local autonomy over considerable fields adds greatly to desirable political pluralism and greatly restricts the power of control, sometimes indirectly-elected controls, so fulfilling the demands of that ancient democratic stalwart, de Tocqueville, for a truer and safer democracy. Where governors and governed are the same, general participation in the social art is indeed *ipso facto* obtained in the consequent awakening of the social consciousness. And, even without "Kensan," communal living in a face-to-face group of its own accord increases personal interaction and, is bound to intensify and crystallize personal social outlook. The moral failure of official twentieth-century "Communism" undoubtedly lay in its inability to induce social purpose in the peoples concerned. Imposition from above is not induction. The latter is the essential which the kibbutz can give (and a central government cannot) by self-education through action. If soviets and communes in the lands in question had been used as apparently original ideals demanded (but which were thrust aside as too difficult and too slow), how different the results might have been! The potentiality for cooperation always exists in human nature, or man would never have achieved humanity at all; but it must be fostered so as to well up naturally from its personality founts. Edicts, supported by force, merely kill it. The secret lies in social education, which the West mainly ignored and which the East, inevitably self-defeatingly, tried to impose *en bloc*. Education is a necessarily gentle process; one has to instill it by persuasion, gradually modifying the brain-field. It is quite impossible to hammer it in. But it took a long time for those Eastern Bloc peoples to come to the right conclusion and start using the kibbutz for the superb educational instrument it is. Nowadays, we simply could not do without it as just that. It is the perfect instrument for social education, spreading its beneficial influence right through society by reason of a few of its members working outside their kibbutzim from time to time and being responsible for a great deal of social organization work, as well as cultural activity, initiated in the kibbutz and imitated and extended elsewhere.

# Postscript

And what of the Jews? We have shown how, in their hands, their very ancient religion (Judaism)—so heavily imbued with social ethics—gave rise, in one sector, to Zionism as the idealism activating their twentieth century return to Zion. The resultant resettlement gave birth to the Israeli kibbutz. They eventually, and with much difficulty, achieved peace with their Semitic cousins, clearing the way for rapid development of that Middle East region. A period strongly reminiscent of a previous golden age of Jewish-Arab cooperation ensued.

Those Jews who did not "return to Zion" were eventually engulfed among the other peoples of the world and finally disappeared as Jews altogether. In that twentieth century, many had deluded themselves into thinking they could carry on indefinitely in exile. By the second third of that century, fewer than twenty per cent of these people gathered to their land; most remained outside. In view of this refusal of the majority to relinquish their existing social conveniences, the Land of Israel was, at one stage, publicly announced as an internationalist land of refuge for all those fleeing from inhuman "humanity," for political refugees and other spiritually homeless persons rebelling against conventional nationalism and imbued with the desire for world citizenship. While the influx was not wholesale, it added considerable elements which prove of utmost worth in forwarding the realization of those very ancient prophetic values which afterwards made the Jews world famous in history.

The assimilation of the Jews into the cultures in which they remained was only part of a very general international process of acculturation. This breaking down of national, cultural, and racial barriers was a necessary preliminary to the social structure which presently exists. One Jewish rabbi of the twentieth century foresaw the results of this process very clearly. We feel it most appropriate to reproduce here his memorable expression of opinion:

> . . .it is years in the future. Jews no longer exist as an entity.
> The Jewish people have disappeared. Jewish festivals and fasts,
> feasts and Holy Days are ancient history, never practiced.
> Synagogues, those that remain, are maintained as historic relics of
> the past. Judaism, the Jewish people, Jewishness have not
> survived. But neither has Christianity, Buddhism, Bahai, or any
> other religion. Men live together in peace and harmony, obeying
> God's law. They respect one another; they care for one another.
> God speaks, they listen. All men automatically teach what is right
> to their children. And, because of the society in which they are
> brought up, the children listen. People do pray in field, while
> fishing, at home, and on the roadside. They don't say they will.
> In every corner of the Universe there is Justice, Righteousness,
> and Mercy. Mankind has finally recognised the Divine within him.
> Judaism has disappeared. What have we lost, really?

While even our own advanced age cannot lay claim to ultimate achievement of the goals set forth here, we can take pride in the fact that our society is at least oriented to the goal of ultimate human development. We also must recognize that the social circumstances which allow us to pursue this worthwhile course must, in part, trace their roots back to the endeavors of those in the twentieth century who foresaw, if dimly, the only possible satisfactory course of human growth.

We should like to conclude with one more quotation from the period under review, one which sums up as completely as could well be done a thousand years ago the position of man in general. We began this survey with a quotation from the same man; we return to him again for our finale. Here, from *Man and Himself*, by Erich Fromm:

> Self-awareness, reason, and imagination have disrupted the
> 'harmony' which characterizes animal existence. Their emergence
> has made man into an anomaly, into the freak of the universe. He
> is part of nature, subject to her physical laws and unable to
> change them, yet he transcends the rest of nature. . . .Being aware
> of himself, he realises his powerlessness and the limitations of his
> existence. Never is he free from the dichotomy of his existence;

he cannot rid himself of his mind, even if he should want to; he cannot rid himself of his body as long as he is alive—and his body makes him want to be alive. Reason, man's blessing, is also his curse; it forces him to cope everlastingly with the task of solving an insoluble dichotomy. Human existence is different in this respect from that of all other organisms; it is in a state of constant and unavoidable disequilibrium... Man is the only animal that can be bored, that can be discontented, that can feel evicted from paradise... There is no innate 'drive for progress' in man; it is the contradiction in his existence that makes him proceed on the way he set out. Having lost paradise, the unity with nature, he has become the eternal wanderer... He must give account to himself of himself, and of the meaning of his existence. He is driven to overcome this inner split, tormented by a craving for 'absoluteness,' for another kind of harmony which can lift the curse by which he was separated from nature, from his fellow men, and from himself... He makes the attempt to restore this unity and equilibrium in the first place in thought by constructing an all-inclusive mental picture of the world which serves as a frame of reference from which he can derive an answer to the question of where he stands and what he ought to do. But such thought-systems are not sufficient. If man were only a disembodied intellect his aim would be achieved by a comprehensive thought-system. But since he is an entity endowed with a body as well as a mind he has to react to the dichotomy of his existence not only in thinking but also in the process of living, in his feelings and actions. He has to strive for the experience of unity and oneness in all spheres of his being in order to find a new equilibrium. Hence any satisfying system of orientation implies not only intellectual elements but elements of feeling and sense to be realised in action in all fields of human endeavour. Devotion to an aim or an idea, or a power transcending man such as God, is an expression of this need for completeness in the process of living...

The split between our sheep nature and our human nature is the basis for two kinds of orientations, the orientation by proximity to the herd and the orientation by reason. Rationalisation is a compromise between our sheep nature and our human capacity to think. The ambiguity of thinking, the dichotomy between reason and a rationalising intellect, is the expression of a basic dichotomy in man, the co-extensive need for bondage and freedom. . .

For the vast majority of men who are not heroes, the development of reason depends on the emergence of a social order in which each individual is fully respected and not made a tool by the State or by any other group, a social order in which he need not be afraid to criticise, and in which the pursuit of truth does not isolate man from his brothers, but makes him feel one with them. It follows that man will attain the full capacity for objectivity and reason only when a society of man is established above all particular divisions of the human race, when loyalty to the human race and to its ideals is considered the prime loyalty that exists.

# Acknowledgements

From THE SANE SOCIETY by Erich Fromm. Copyright © 1955 by Erich Fromm. Reprinted by permission of Holt, Rinehart and Winston, Inc., and Routledge & Kegan Paul Ltd., London. (7-9, 144-145)

From ETHICS OF COMPETITION AND OTHER ESSAYS by Frank Knight. Copyright © by Frank H. Knight. Reprinted by permission of George Allen & Unwin, Ltd. (12-15)

From THE MORALITY OF PUNISHMENT by A. C. Ewing. Copyright © by A. C. Ewing. Reprinted by permission of Routledge & Kegan Paul Ltd., London. (20-21)

From REASON IN POLITICS by Prof. K. Smellie. Copyright © by Prof. K. Smellie. Reprinted by permission of Gerald Duckworth & Co. Ltd. (21)

From REFLECTIONS ON THE REVOLUTION OF OUR TIME by Harold Laski. Copyright © by Harold Laski. Reprinted by permission of George Allen & Unwin, Ltd., and The Viking Press, Inc. (22-24)

From RAIN UPON GODSHILL by J. B. Priestley. Copyright © by J. B. Priestley. Reprinted by permission of A. D. Peters & Co. (29-30, 57, 58)

From CIVILIZATION AND ETHICS by Dr. Albert Schweitzer. Copyright © by Dr. Albert Schweitzer. Reprinted by permission of A. C. Black Ltd. (30)

From SOCIOLOGY AND PHILOSOPHY by Emile Durkheim. Copyright © Emile Durkheim. (51-52)

From METHODS FOR EXPERIMENTAL SOCIAL INNOVATION by Prof. George W. Fairweather. Copyright © Prof. George W. Fairweather. Reprinted by permission of John Wiley & Sons, Inc. (55)

From MAN, MORALS AND SOCIETY by J. C. Flugel. Copyright © by J. C. Flugel. Reprinted by permission of Gerald Duckworth & Co. Ltd., and International Universities Press. (56)

From ESSAYS OF A BIOLOGIST by Julian Huxley. Copyright © by Julian Huxley. Reprinted by permission of A. D. Peters & Co. (60)

From THE SHAPE OF THINGS TO COME by H. G. Wells. Reprinted by permission of the Estate of H. G. Wells, Collins-Knowlton-Wing, Inc. Copyright © 1933 by George Philip Wells and Francis Philip Wells, and 1970 by the Estate of H. G. Wells. (106-109)

From A MODERN UTOPIA by H. G. Wells. Reprinted by permission of the Estate of H. G. Wells, Collins-Knowlton-Wing, Inc. Copyright © 1905 by George Philip Wells and Francis Philip Wells, and 1970 by the Estate of H. G. Wells. (104-105)

From MARRIAGE by H. G. Wells. Reprinted by permission of the Estate of H. G. Wells, Dodd, Mead & Co. Copyright © 1912 by George Philip Wells and Francis Philip Wells, and 1970 by the Estate of H. G. Wells. (102-103)

From BABES IN A DARKLING WOOD by H. G. Wells. Reprinted by permission of the Estate of H. G. Wells. Copyright © 1940 by George Philip Wells and Francis Philip Wells, and 1970 by the Estate of H. G. Wells. (100-102)

From THE LAST AND FIRST MEN by Olaf Stapledon. Copyright © by Olaf Stapledon. Reprinted by permission of Methuen & Co., Ltd. (106)

From SOCIETY by Robert M. MacIver. Copyright © by Robert M. MacIver. Reprinted by permission of Holt, Rinehart and Winston, Inc. (114-115)

From METAPHYSICAL THEORY OF THE STATE by L. T. Hobhouse. Copyright © by L. T. Hobhouse. Reprinted by permission of George Allen & Unwin, Ltd. and Barnes and Noble, Inc. (116)

From THE TWO SOURCES OF MORALITY AND RELIGION by Henri Bergson, translated by R. Ashley Audra and Cloudesley Brereton. Copyright © by Henri Bergson. Reprinted by permission of Holt, Rinehart and Winston, Inc. (116-117)

From BARBARIANS AT THE GATE by Leonard Woolf, 1939. Copyright © by Leonard Woolf. Reprinted by permission of Victor Gollancz Ltd., London. (117)

From DEMOCRATIC IDEALS AND REALITY by H. J. Mackinder. Copyright © by H. J. Mackinder. Reprinted by permission of Constable and Co. Ltd., London. (127, 146-147)

Dorothy Thompson for her article, "I Believe; Ten Articles of Faith." (147)

From THE PRESS THE PUBLIC WANTS by Kingsley Martin. Copyright © by the Estate of Kingsley Martin. Reprinted by permission of The Hogarth Press, Ltd. (148)

Reprinted by permission of Faber and Faber Ltd. from *The Philosophy of Communism* by John Macmurray. (149-151)

From THIEVES IN THE NIGHT by Arthur Koestler. Copyright © by Arthur Koestler. Reprinted by permission of A. D. Peters & Co. (151-152)

From MAN FOR HIMSELF by Erich Fromm. Copyright © 1947 by Erich Fromm. Reprinted by permission of Holt, Rinehart and Winston, Inc. and Routledge & Kegan Paul Ltd., London. (160-162)

## Analysis of Contemporary Culture

**The Black Seventies**
Floyd B. Barbour, ed. — From the editor of the
*Black Power Revolt* comes a series of original essays
by and for the Black community. Members of the
community discuss future relationships to art,
science, literature, technology, and education. A
new, provocative, enlightening challenge to traditional white and black thought on the black experience.                    300 pp.   $6 cloth   $3 paper

**The New Left: A Collection of Essays**
Priscilla Long, ed. — 29 essays provide original in-
sight into the nature of the movement, its tactics,
strategy, and ultimate goals. Included are Frank
Joyce on racism, Rudolf Rocker on anarchism,
Howard Zinn on Marxism, and many more.
                         500 pp.   $6 cloth   $3 paper

**The Black Power Revolt**
Floyd B. Barbour, ed. — Black authors from Nat
Turner to Stokely Carmichael trace the concept of
Black Power from past to present. Included are Leroi
Jones, Chuck Stone, Malcolm X, Floyd McKissick,
and others. These essays have been acclaimed for
their honesty and reality of perception by educators
throughout the country.          288 pp.   $5.95

**Marx and Keynes:**
**The Limits of the Mixed Economy**
Paul Mattick — A critical evaluation of the functioning of major economic thought. This work analyzes
the limitations and potential failures of mixed systems, and points to the need of new means to resolve
inherent economic problems.      350 pp.   $6.95

**Democracy and Non-Violence**
Ralph T. Templin — An examination of the nature of
racism, pacifism, nationalism, and revolution which
views with honesty and concern our outmoded atti-
tudes and institutions and deals with the question of
achieving peace in a world of violence.   336 pp.   $4

**Power and Morality**
Pitirim A. Sorokin and Walter Lunden — Viewing power from an historical perspective, the authors present a compelling case for the elimination of our fear-ridden social structures with their potentiality for total destruction, and their replacement by a new social order dedicated to building a creative and noble civilization. 200 pp. $3.50

## Social Studies and Integrative Works

**The Nature of Civilizations**
Matthew Melko — An innovative approach to comparative history which draws on the work of Coulbourn, Spengler, and Toynbee (among others) to define and construct a basic model of civilization. The author then views current Western civilization in this light and predicts its future possibilities.
224 pp. $4.95

**Toynbee and History**
M. F. Ashley Montagu, ed.—P. Geyl, Renier, Trevor-Roper, Kenneth Thompson, Sorokin, and other experts in fields covered in Toynbee's monumental *A Study of History* examine the nature of his contributions and permit the reader his own conclusions as to the value of Toynbee's efforts. 385 pp. $5

**Anthropology and Human Nature**
M. F. Ashley Montagu — Anthropology is related to the nature of human nature, race, medicine, sexual development, crime, and other aspects of civilization, with the theme of anthropology as the bridge between science and the humanities. 390 pp. $6

**Mutual Aid**
Petr Kropotkin — Kropotkin's classic answer to the misuse of the theory of "survival of the fittest." The author presents the progressive elements of evolution, cooperation and support within the species, as a basis for social growth. 400 pp. $4 cloth $2 paper

**The Integration of Human Knowledge**
Oliver L. Reiser — A philosophy of Scientific Humanism that is challenging, controversial, and creative. Dr. Reiser advocates a synthesis of science and

philosophy and a re-evaluation of man's knowledge of himself and the sciences. A new approach to the totality of knowledge.                480 pp.   $8

## The Definition of Definition

Ralph Borsodi — The complexity of modern technology has given rise to increasing difficulties in articulation of problems and solutions, indicating a need for new directions in the study of language and culture. A uniquely rational approach to the integration of knowledge.   128 pp.   $4 cloth   $2 paper

# Sociology

## Values in Human Society

F. R. Cowell — A major review of Sorokin's sociology, leading to two new and significant theories: that sociology and the philosophical theory of value are mutually illuminated from Sorokin's position; and that value judgments in ethics and aesthetics are necessarily circular.                500 pp.   $8.95

## Social and Cultural Dynamics

Pitirim A. Sorokin — The author's own abridgement of his four volume masterpiece, vital to sociological theory. A survey of change in major systems of art, truth, ethics, law, and social relationships throughout history analyzes the trends and events that have made our civilization what it is.        720 pp.   $10.00

## Dialectical Sociology

Dr. Phillip Bosserman — A critical examination of the much-neglected French sociologist, Georges Gurvitch, which surveys his attempt to relate sociology to philosophy and history. A much needed reference work.                336 pp.   $7.95

## Social Work and Social Change

Sugata Dasgupta — A study comparing social and economic development in two sets of Indian villages, contrasting results of traditional social work with those of a new community development program (developed in part by Rabindranath Tagore) which advocates the integration of social change into the social, economic, and religious perceptions of the people.                240 pp.   $6.95

# VERMONT COLLEGE
## MONTPELIER, VERMONT